EVERYD GRAPHS

PICTOGRAMS, BAR CHARTS, PIE CHARTS

LINE GRAPHS

PETER ROBSON

Newby Books

EASINGWOLD TOWN HALL COMPANY LTD
THE ADVERTISER OFFICE, MARKET PLACE,
EASINGWOLD, YORK YO61 3AB
TEL 01347 821329
www.newbybooks.co.uk

PICTOGRAMS, BAR CHARTS, PIE CHARTS, HISTOGRAMS

PICTOGRAMS
(Also called Pictographs)

A pictogram shows information by means of pictures, e.g. The jobs of all the male people over 18 years of age in the town of Haltingham were noted. They were

coal mining	4000 men
office jobs	3000 men
other jobs	2000 men
unemployed	2000 men

A pictogram of this information would look something like this:-

COAL MINING   👤 👤 👤 👤   <u>Pictogram to show</u>

OFFICE JOBS   👤 👤 👤   <u>jobs of men in</u>

OTHER JOBS   👤 👤   <u>Haltingham</u>

UNEMPLOYED   👤 👤   (👤   represents 1000 men)

REMEMBER
1) Pictures must all start in a straight line, one underneath the other, and must always occupy the same amount of space as one another (e.g. if squared paper is being used, one picture can occupy one square).
2) A key must be written down to show what each picture represents,

       e.g. 👤   represents 1 girl, 🚗 represents 10 cars, etc.
3) A pictogram should always have a title which explains what the pictogram shows.

Sometimes **half a picture** (or an even smaller fraction) may be used, e.g.
A rose grower sells 600 red roses, 450 yellow roses and 100 white roses.

RED   🌹 🌹 🌹 🌹 🌹 🌹   <u>Pictogram to show</u>

YELLOW   🌹 🌹 🌹 🌹 🌸   <u>sales of roses</u>

WHITE   🌹   (🌹 represents 100 roses)

---

1   This pictogram shows the number of packets of 'Cornies' cereal sold by a supermarket during one week (to the nearest 5 packets each day).

Each 📦 represents 10 packets.

(a) Write down how many packets were sold each day.

(b) What was the total number of packets sold in the week?

MONDAY	📦 📦 📦
TUESDAY	📦 📦 📦 📦
WEDNESDAY	📦 📦
THURSDAY	📦 📦 📦
FRIDAY	📦 📦 📦 📦 📦
SATURDAY	📦 📦 📦 📦 📦

2 A shop sells 20 television sets in June, 15 in July, 30 in August and 35 in September.

Draw a pictogram to show the information.

(Suggestion: 🖥 to represent 5 television sets.)

---

3 The number of balloons at 4 people's parties were:-

Carl..............................30		Liz. 70
Sophie. 40		William. 80

Choose your own picture to represent a certain number of balloons.
Then draw a pictogram to show the information.

4

Chimpanzee's Weekly	
Amateur Grumbling	
Slug and Snail	
Toes Illustrated	

(📰 represents 5000 copies)

The pictogram shows the weekly sales (number of copies sold each week) of four magazines published by a magazine company. Write down the name of each magazine with the number of copies sold.

---

5 Adderbrook Forest has 4 million trees,
Delville Forest has 6 million trees,
Eston Forest has 3½ million trees,
Hillhead Forest has 8 million trees,
Westwick Forest has 5½ million trees.
Choose your own picture to represent a certain number of trees. Then draw a pictogram to show the number of trees in each forest.

---

6 A bus company keeps its buses at five different depots. The list shows the names of the depots and the number of buses at each depot.

Barnbrough. 55		Dunnerby. 15
Firlington. 25		Rywood. 40
Sedgeworth. 50		

Draw a diagram to show this information. (Suggestion: 🚌 to represent 10 buses.)

---

7 A seaside shop is open from 0900 to 1800 (9.00a.m. to 6.00p.m.) each day. On a certain day its sales of ice-cream cones for each hour were

0900 to 1000........10		1400 to 1500......120
1000 to 1100........25		1500 to 1600........95
1100 to 1200........40		1600 to 1700........50
1200 to 1300........75		1700 to 1800........20
1300 to 1400........80		

Choose your own picture to represent a certain number of ice-cream cones. Then draw a pictogram to illustrate the information.

BAR CHARTS

A BAR CHART (or bar graph or block graph) shows information by means of bars made up of blocks (squares or rectangles).

The bars are arranged either horizontally or vertically. When they are arranged vertically, the bar chart is sometimes called a **COLUMN GRAPH.**

A bar chart usually (but not always) has gaps between the bars.

Example

The football XI at Markland Road School played 14 matches during the season.
They won 7, lost 3 and drew 4.

Horizontal bars

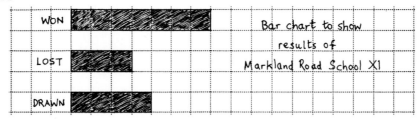

REMEMBER

1) All the bars must start at exactly the same distance from the left.
2) The bars can be any width, but they must all be the same width.
3) The spaces between the bars can be any width, but they must all be the same width.
4) The chart must have a title.

Vertical bars (Column graph)

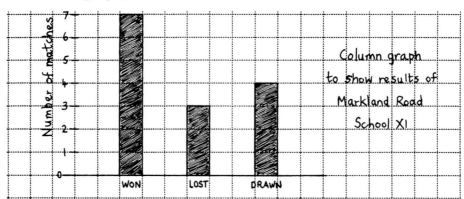

REMEMBER

1) All the columns must start at the same level.
2) The columns can be any width, but they must all be the same width.
3) The spaces between the columns can be any width, but they must all be the same width.
4) The graph must have a title.

Important

If an amount is recorded as ZERO (0) it must be drawn as zero, WITH NO BAR OR COLUMN AT ALL, e.g. Blexborough's team won 4 matches, drew 2 and lost 0, so a column graph of their results would look like

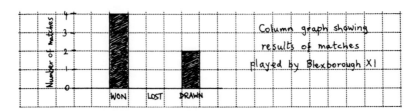

If each block in your diagram represents **more than one thing,** always make sure that you show how many things each block represents, by drawing either (a) a key, or (b) a scale of numbers next to the diagram, e.g.

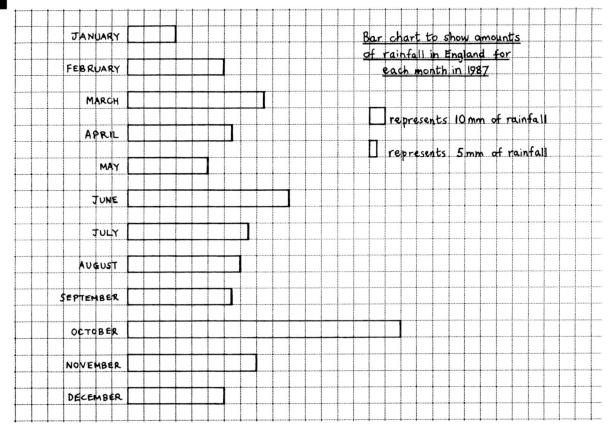

8 Look at the bar chart and answer the questions underneath.

(a)   Which was the driest month?
(b)   Which was the wettest month?
(c)   Which months had 65mm of rainfall?
(d)   How much rainfall was there in March?
(e)   What was the total rainfall for 1987?
(f)   By dividing the total rainfall by the number of months, find the average (or mean) monthly rainfall.
(g)   Which month had nearest to the average monthly rainfall?

9 Glenda's money box contained
7 £1 coins;   3 50p coins,   8 20p coins;   13 10p coins;   6 5p coins;
0 2p coins;   9 1p coins.
(a)   Draw a bar chart to show the amount of coins.
(b)   How much money did Glenda's money box contain altogether?

10 To play a certain symphony, an orchestra needs 44 string instruments, 16 woodwind instruments, 12 brass instruments and 8 percussion instruments. Draw a bar chart to show how many of each kind of instrument are required. (Suggestion: 1 block could represent 4 instruments. Remember to show how many instruments each block represents.)

11 There were 4 candidates in a school election. Their names, and the number of people voting for each candidate, were

Annabelle Large	73
Bunty Small	28
Charlotte Short	82
Deborah Long	44

Draw a bar chart to show this information. (Suggestion: 1 block could represent 10 votes.)

12 The bar chart shows the areas, in hectares (to the nearest 10000 hectares) of the Welsh counties.

Each square 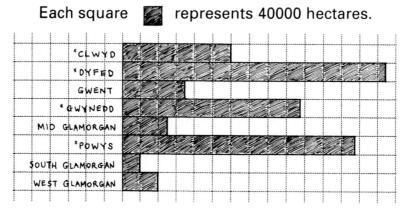 represents 40000 hectares.

(a)   What area does half a square ▌ represent?
(b)   What area does three quarters of a square ▓ represent?
(c)   From the bar chart, find the area of each county.

*Note. Names are pronounced (roughly): <u>Kloo</u>-id, <u>Duvv</u>-ed, <u>Gwinn</u>-eth (with a th like the beginning of the word 'the'), <u>Pow</u>-iss (first part like 'cow').

How to find the AVERAGE (or MEAN) from a bar chart

e.g. This is a column graph to show the distance travelled (to the nearest 10 miles) each day of the Southwood family's holidays, starting on Sunday and finishing on Saturday.

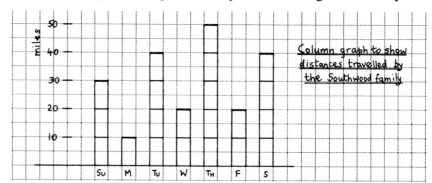

Where could you draw a straight line across the graph so that the number of blocks sticking up above the line was equal to the number of gaps below the line?

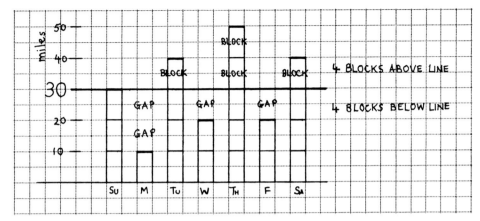

The line would be at 30 miles, so the AVERAGE (or MEAN) distance travelled each day was 30 miles.

13 The column graph shows the number of hours of sunshine (to the nearest hour) recorded at a certain town in the month of May. The horizontal axis shows the date in May, and the vertical axis shows the number of hours of sunshine (to the nearest hour) recorded. On the 1st of May, 8 hours were recorded; on the 2nd of May, 7 hours were recorded, etc.

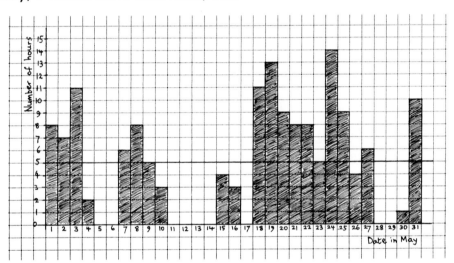

(a)   Which day had the most sunshine?
(b)   On how many days were 0 hours of sunshine recorded?
(c)   On which dates were 8 hours recorded?
(d)   What was the total number of hours recorded during the month of May?
(e)   What does the horizontal line at 5 hours represent? Count the number of shaded squares above the line, and then count the number of unshaded squares below the line. What do you notice?
(f)   On the 15th of May, what is the longest amount of sunshine there could have been? (Remember the graph shows amounts of sunshine to the nearest hour.)

14 During the last week of October, Terry ate the following number of toffees:-
Monday 3, Tuesday 5, Wednesday 2, Thursday 4, Friday 0, Saturday 6, Sunday 8.
(a)   Construct a column graph to show this information.
(b)   Draw a horizontal line on the column graph to show the average (mean) daily consumption of toffees.

15

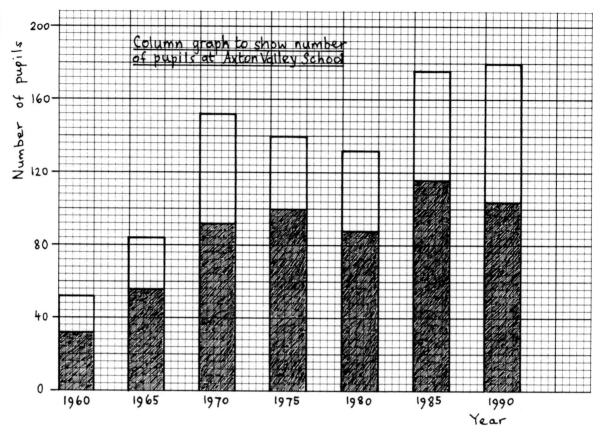

The column graph shows the number of pupils at Axton Valley School (to the nearest 4 pupils) every 5 years from 1960 to 1990. The shaded part of each column represents boarding pupils; the unshaded part represents day pupils.

(a) How many pupils does each small square on the vertical axis represent?

(b) How many pupils did the school have in these years?
     (i) 1965   (ii) 1975   (iii) 1985

(c) How many boarding pupils did the school have in these years?
     (i) 1960   (ii) 1970   (iii) 1985

(d) How many day pupils did the school have in these years?
     (i) 1965   (ii) 1980   (iii) 1990.

TIME CHARTS

A time chart is a kind of bar chart to show when things start and finish. It can be useful for showing how each event compares with the others, which events are happening at the same time, etc.

16 This is a list of 10 events in a village show. Next to each event are the times of day when the event started and finished. Copy, on to 2mm graph paper, the names and axes shown at the top of page 9 (Your squares will be a bit larger than the ones in this diagram). Then draw a bar for each event in its correct place (Pets competition has already been done as an example.).

Archery competition	1630 to 1830		Livestock judging	1400 to 1530
Barbecue	1830 to 2030		Pets competition	1600 to 1700
Disco dance	1930 to 2200		Sheepdog trials	1300 to 1730
Four wheel drive vehicle display	1530 to 1630		Shire horse parade	1330 to 1430
Fruit & veg. judging	1300 to 1430		Silver band concert	1500 to 1600

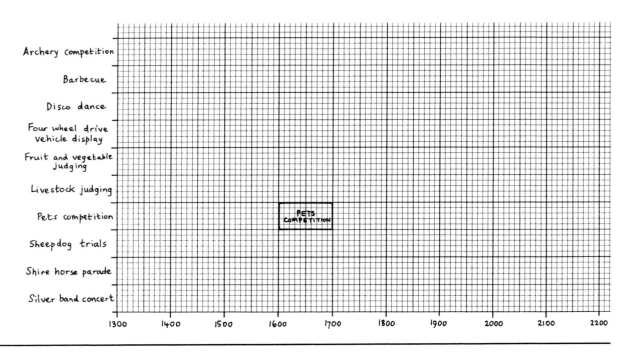

17 This list gives the names of ten writers and the dates when each writer was born and died (e.g. Enid Blyton was born in 1897 and died in 1968).

Enid Blyton	1897-1968	Beatrix Potter	1866-1943
Roald Dahl	1916-1990	Arthur Ransome	1884-1967
Charles Dickens	1812-1870	Anna Sewell	1820-1878
C.S. Lewis	1898-1963	R.L. Stevenson	1850-1894
A.A. Milne	1882-1956	J.R.R. Tolkien	1892-1973

(a) Copy on to 2mm graph paper the axes and names of writers as shown in the diagram below (Your squares will be a bit larger than these).

(b) Complete the time chart (A.A. Milne has already been done as an example).

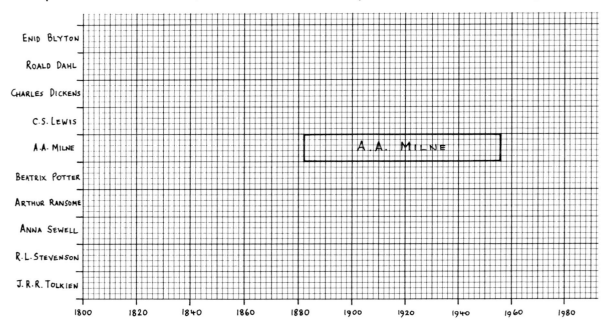

(c) Each of these books was written by a different writer in the list. Can you fit the books to the correct writers?
Black Beauty, Charlie and the Chocolate Factory, Coot Club, Five on a Secret Trail, The Hobbit, The Horse and his Boy, Oliver Twist, The Tale of Peter Rabbit, Treasure Island, Winnie-the-Pooh.

FREQUENCY CHARTS (Distribution Tables)

The frequency of a thing means how many times the thing occurs (or happens).

A FREQUENCY CHART shows the frequency distribution, or how many times each kind of thing occurs. Each different kind of thing is called a CLASS.

It is sometimes useful to make a frequency chart before drawing a statistical diagram (bar chart, pie chart, histogram, etc.).

Example (1)

The number of days in each month of the year (not a leap year) are

January............31	April...............30	July.................31	October 31
February.........28	May.................31	August............31	November 30
March............31	June...............30	September 30	December.......31

There is only 1 month with 28 days, there are 4 months with 30 days, and 7 months with 31 days. A frequency chart would look something like this

Number of days in month	28	30	31	← CLASS
Number of months	1	4	7	← FREQUENCY

Example (2)

The modern Olympic Games (from 1896 to 2012) have taken place (or will take place) in four different continents:-

1896	Europe	1928	Europe	1964	Asia	1992	Europe
1900	Europe	1932	N.America	1968	N.America	1996	N.America
1904	N.America	1936	Europe	1972	Europe	2000	Australia
1908	Europe	1948	Europe	1976	N.America	2004	Europe
1912	Europe	1952	Europe	1980	Europe	2008	Asia
1920	Europe	1956	Australia	1984	N.America	2012	Europe
1924	Europe	1960	Europe	1988	Asia		

Make a frequency chart to show the above information.

Continent	Asia	Australia	Europe	N. America
Frequency	3	2	16	6

NOTE. It is a good idea to check that the <u>total number</u> of things in the frequency chart and in the original list is the same, in case you have mis-counted.

Tally marks

If there is a large number of similar things to count for a frequency chart, it is sometimes helpful to use tally marks. For each thing counted, one mark is drawn

1 thing	I
2 things	II
3 things	III
4 things	IIII

For the fifth thing, a horizontal line is drawn through the other four marks.

5 things	⤕⤕⤕
6 things	⤕⤕⤕ I
7 things	⤕⤕⤕ II , etc.

When a total is made, the <u>groups of five</u> can be seen easily, e.g.

HHH HHH I I I = 13

HHH HHH HHH I = 16, etc.

Example

Make a tally of the number of times A, B, C and D occur in this collection

D B B C D A C B A B
C D B C C B A D D A
B C A A C C B D B C
B A D D A B C A C C

Letter	Tally	Total (Frequency)
A	HHH I I I I	9
B	HHH HHH I	11
C	HHH HHH I I	12
D	HHH I I I	8

18 Write down the number shown by each of these tallies

(a) HHH HHH I I I I

(b) HHH HHH HHH I I

(c) HHH HHH HHH HHH HHH I

(d) HHH HHH

(e) HHH HHH HHH HHH I I

19 Copy and complete this chart.

Tally	Frequency
HHH HHH I I I	
	20
HHH HHH HHH HHH HHH HHH HHH I I I I	
HHH HHH HHH HHH HHH I I	
	33

20 The tickets for a show had different colours depending on the kind of person buying them:- adults: yellow (Y), senior citizens: blue (B), children: red (R), foreign visitors: green (G). The first 50 tickets sold had the following colours:-

Y B Y Y R Y Y Y R B
B Y Y R R R Y Y G G
Y Y R R B B R R Y Y
Y B R Y R R R Y Y G
G G G Y Y R B R R Y

Copy and complete this tally and frequency chart.

Ticket colour	Tally	Total (Frequency)
YELLOW		
BLUE		
RED		
GREEN		

21 In the following sentence, some words have 1 letter, some have 2, some have 3, etc.

SCROOGE LAY IN THIS STATE UNTIL THE CHIME HAD GONE THREE QUARTERS MORE, WHEN HE REMEMBERED, ON A SUDDEN, THAT THE GHOST HAD WARNED HIM OF A VISITATION WHEN THE BELL TOLLED ONE.

Make a chart to show the frequency of words with 1,2,3,4,5,6,7,8,9 and 10 letters. Begin like this:-

Number of letters in word	1	2	3	4
Frequency				

22 The heights, in centimetres, of 20 people on a school camp were

98	142	117	130
151	155	142	153
180	115	165	178
146	133	108	123
137	173	123	144

Copy and complete this frequency chart.

Height	Shorter than 101 cm	101 to 120 cm	121 to 140 cm	141 to 160 cm	Taller than 160 cm
Number of People					

23 Two dice were shaken 100 times and the scores were written down.

2	10	4	9	12	5	9	8	7	7
3	7	8	7	11	9	4	8	2	11
8	3	7	7	9	6	8	8	12	10
7	12	9	6	5	11	9	8	6	4
7	10	3	8	2	8	9	5	3	2
5	8	6	6	10	9	7	7	6	12
8	6	8	12	4	7	10	5	6	7
7	6	9	5	11	11	4	6	10	5
9	2	8	9	3	7	8	2	8	7
5	7	7	10	9	11	8	9	8	7

(a) Make a frequency chart to show these scores (Use tally marks if you wish).

SCORE	2	3	
FREQUENCY				etc.

(b) Try shaking two dice 100 times. Make a frequency chart and see how it compares with this one.

(c) Which score is likely to occur more than any others?

24 The ages of 50 children playing in a playground were

10	11	9	7	11	8	12	9	10	8
11	8	8	9	10	11	7	8	9	11
9	11	7	10	12	8	9	10	9	8
9	7	9	9	7	9	8	9	7	9
11	10	8	11	9	10	11	12	10	8

(a) Count the number of children of each age, and make a frequency chart

Age	7	8	9	10	11	12
Number of children (Frequency)						

(b) Draw a bar chart to show how many children there were of each age.
(c) Using the same information, make a new frequency chart, grouping together ages 7 and 8 in one total, 9 and 10 in another, 11 and 12 in another.

Age	7 and 8	9 and 10	11 and 12
Frequency			

(d) Draw a bar chart based on your new frequency chart.

---

25 Here are the results of a season of football matches played in the Hilltop League. Each line represents one match. The home team is on the left.

St George's	1	Orton Grove	3
Forest Park	2	Newton Junior	2
Westway	0	St George's	0
Orton Grove	2	Forest Park	3
Newton Junior	3	Westway	2
St George's	2	Forest Park	3
Orton Grove	3	Newton Junior	3
Forest Park	2	Westway	1
Newton Junior	2	St George's	1
Westway	4	Orton Grove	1
Orton Grove	0	Westway	1
Newton Junior	5	Forest Park	0
Forest Park	2	St George's	4
Westway	0	Newton Junior	4
St George's	2	Westway	0
Forest Park	4	Orton Grove	4
St George's	4	Newton Junior	3
Westway	3	Forest Park	2
Orton Grove	8	St George's	2
Newton Junior	2	Orton Grove	1

For example, the first line shows a match between St George's and Orton Grove, played at St George's ground. St George's scored 1 goal; Orton Grove scored 3 goals. The result was an away win because the 'away' or 'visiting' team won the match.

Using the results of the matches, try these questions:-

(a) How many different teams played in the league?
(b) Make a list of the teams. Then write against each team the total number of goals the team scored.
(c) Draw a bar chart to illustrate the information in question (b).
(d) (i)   How many matches resulted in home wins?
    (ii) How many matches resulted in away wins?
    (iii) How many matches were drawn?
(e) Draw a bar chart showing home wins, away wins and draws.
(f) Which team were the champions (Which team won the most matches)?
(g) How many matches had <u>no goals</u> at all?
    How many mathces had only ONE goal?
    How many matches had TWO goals?
    Continue the list, noting how many matches had 3,4,5,6,7,8,9 and 10 goals.
(h) Draw a frequency chart to show the information in (g). Start the chart like this:-

Number of goals in a match	0	1	2	3	etc.
Number of matches with this number of goals					

(i) Draw a bar chart to show the information in (h).
(j) Next season, an extra team called Birch Hall will join the Hilltop League. How many matches will have to be played altogether if every team plays every other team once at home and once away?

HISTOGRAMS

A HISTOGRAM is a special kind of block graph used for <u>continuous data</u> (where the information goes up and down gradually, instead of in single units).

A histogram looks rather like a column graph with no gaps, but it has a <u>horizontal axis</u> (a line going along the bottom) divided into equal sections.

Example

The first 20 customers paying at Brenda's check-out in the supermarket spent these amounts

£ 2.58	£ 0.58	£47.58	£20.76
£ 5.20	£ 7.25	£21.02	£ 8.19
£16.16	£24.97	£13.72	£42.83
£ 8.43	£10.35	£ 1.80	£17.05
£35.85	£ 6.81	£28.64	£22.92

(a) Make a frequency chart with these classes (groups):-

£ 0.00	to	£ 9.99
£10.00	to	£19.99
£20.00	to	£29.99
£30.00	to	£39.99
£40.00	to	£49.99

For example, the amounts from £10.00 to £19.99 are
            £16.16,   £10.35,   £13.72,   £17.05
so the number of customers (frequency) is 4.

Amount	£0.00 to £9.99	£10.00 to £19.99	£20.00 to £29.99	£30.00 to £39.99	£40.00 to £49.99
Number of customers	8	4	5	1	2

(b) Draw a histogram to show this information.

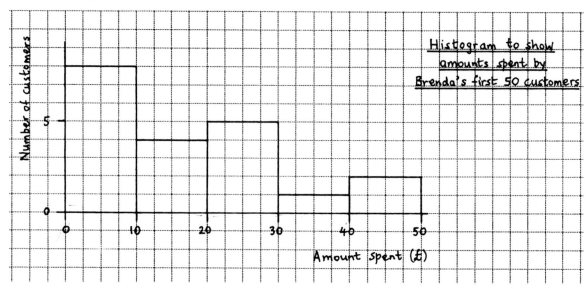

[NOTE. Especially for more advanced histograms (not in this book) it is important to remember that it is the AREA of each column which really shows the information (not always the height).]

26 The salaries of eighteen people attending a conference were (to the nearest £25)

£14350	£27100	£ 9375
£16500	£14625	£22000
£13375	£13675	£11875
£ 4900	£ 9850	£26800
£18800	£32300	£15025
£12950	£17500	£25175

(a) Copy and complete this frequency chart.

Salary	£0 to £4999	£5000 to £9999	£10000 to £14999	£15000 to £19999	£20000 to £24999	£25000 to £29999	£30000 to £34999
Number of people	1	2	6	4	1	3	1

(b) Copy and complete this histogram to show the information. The squares do not have to be the same size as these.

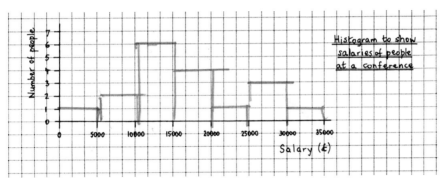

27 Between 1300 and 1700 hours, 30 trains left a station. Their times of departure (leaving) were

1300	1352	1424	1512	1606	1625
1310	1352	1427	1534	1610	1633
1320	1358	1438	1545	1618	1640
1331	1405	1445	1550	1618	1645
1345	1413	1505	1602	1620	1653

(a) Compile a frequency chart with these classes

1300 to 1359
1400 to 1459
1500 to 1559
1600 to 1659

Y : Time   X : No. of trains

(b) From the information in your completed frequency chart, draw a histogram with 2 cm for each column width, and marked 1300, 1400, 1500, 1600, 1700.

28 This list shows the masses, in kg, of members of a group of people.

48.1	70.4	32.7	56.9	44.6
63.9	33.1	18.7	19.6	61.0
27.4	72.2	60.1	37.0	66.3
55.0	93.3	83.2	81.2	
49.8	40.3	53.8	39.3	

(a) Make a frequency chart with classes:-
      0 to 19.9kg, 20.0 to 39.9 kg, 40.0 to 59.9kg, 60.0 to 79.9kg, 80.0 to 99.9kg.
(b) Draw a histogram to show the information.

29 A company sends parcels to its customers. One day it sent 20 parcels. The masses of the parcels, in kg correct to 1 decimal place, were

| 3.5 | 6.2 | 1.8 | 8.4 | 7.1 | 3.8 | 4.3 | 11.2 | 6.6 | 5.0 |

| 4.2 | 7.7 | 10.5 | 9.2 | 6.3 | 11.6 | 5.9 | 2.7 | 7.0 | 4.7 |

(a)   Copy and complete this frequency chart.

		A	B	C	D	E	F
		0 to 1.9 kg	2.0 to 3.9 kg	4.0 to 5.9 kg	6.0 to 7.9 kg	8.0 to 9.9 kg	10.0 to 11.9 kg
Mass of parcel							
Number of parcels							

(b)   Draw a histogram to show the information in the frequency chart.

(c)   Parcels in column A cost £2 each to send
              column B cost £3 each to send
              column C cost £4 each to send
              column D cost £5 each to send
              column E cost £6 each to send
              column F cost £7 each to send
     How much did it cost to send all the day's parcels?

30 The percentage marks achieved by 40 pupils in an exam were

48	68	65	36	88	52	59	43	63	11
52	81	36	75	27	64	38	70	84	45
62	31	84	56	45	91	67	61	59	18
83	52	77	42	68	51	33	81	57	63

(a)   Make a frequency chart with these classes:-
     0 but less than 20 (0 to 19)
     20 but less than 40 (20 to 39)
     40 but less than 60 (40 to 59)
     60 but less than 80 (60 to 79)
     80 but less than 100 (80 to 99).

(b)   Draw a histogram to show the information in the frequency chart.
     Mark the horizontal axis of the histogram 0,20,40,60,80,100 %.

31 These are the distances, in miles, walked by 50 people on a sponsored walk.

17	28	8	26	35	12	35	3	23	18
35	14	17	30	19	19	24	10	35	32
5	25	27	12	17	14	35	35	23	28
18	13	35	29	28	35	11	27	23	20
16	35	30	3	21	25	8	17	6	31

(a)   Make a frequency chart with these classes:- 0.5 to 5.5 miles,
     5.6 to 10.5 miles, 10.6 to 15.5. miles, 15.6 to 20.5 miles, 20.6 to 25.5 miles,
     25.6 to 30.5 miles, 30.6 to 35.5. miles.

(b)   Construct a histogram. Use two squares on the horizontal axis to represent
     5 miles, and mark the axis as shown:-

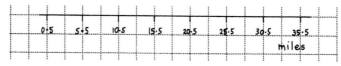

PIE CHARTS

In a pie chart, the amounts are shown as sectors of a circle, or slices of a circular pie.

> THE KEY TO SUCCESS WITH PIE CHARTS IS 360 DEGREES (360°)
> because there are 360° in a revolution (all the way round).

How to draw a pie chart

e.g., Draw a pie chart to show where members of a group of people went on holiday.

U.K. 5 people, **Spain** 3 people, **France** 2 people, **Denmark** 1 person, **U.S.A.** 1 person.

1) Find the TOTAL number of things you wish to put in the chart (In this example, they are PEOPLE)

$$5 + 3 + 2 + 1 + 1 = 12$$

2) Divide 360° by this number to find the angle needed for each thing

$$\frac{360°}{12} = 30°$$

3) Calculate each sector, using the angle you have found

U.K.	5 people	5 x 30° = 150°
Spain	3 people	3 x 30° = 90°
France	2 people	2 x 30° = 60°
Denmark	1 person	1 x 30° = 30°
U.S.A.	1 person	1 x 30° = 30°

When you have done this, check that the angles add up to 360°.

4) Draw a circle and a radius (straight line from centre to outside).
A handy-sized pie chart for an ordinary page needs a radius of between 5 and 7 cm, bigger than the one shown here.

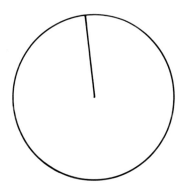

5) Using a protractor, draw the first sector.

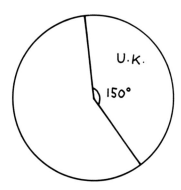

6)   Placing the protractor on your new radius, draw the next sector

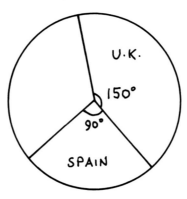

7)   Keep going until all the information has been put in the chart.
      It does not matter in which order the sectors are drawn, nor which way round they go, as
      long as they are all the correct size.

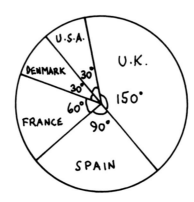

Pie chart to show
where members of
a group of people
went on holiday.

8)   Make sure each sector is labelled correctly (i.e. it has the correct name in it) and always give
      your pie chart a title to explain what information it is showing.
      Pie charts can often be made more effective by <u>colouring the different sectors</u> in different
      colours. Use contrasting colours for adjacent (next door) sectors, and try not to put blue next
      to green, or red next to orange. (Warning. Felt pens sometimes make a mess, so coloured
      pencils are probably more likely to be neat.)

e.g. (2) A certain country's exports during a certain year were worth:-

oil	$7000000	(or $7 million)
cotton	$4500000	(or $4.5 million)
carpets	$2500000	(or $2.5 million)
other things	$1000000	(or $1 million)

Draw a pie chart to show this information.

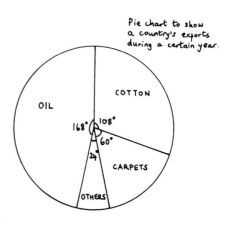

Pie chart to show
a country's exports
during a certain year.

1)   Total number of things
      7 + 4.5 + 2.5 + 1 = 15 million dollars
2)   Sector needed for each 1 million dollars
      $$\frac{360°}{15} = 24°$$
3)   Sectors

oil	7	x	24°	=	168°
cotton	4.5	x	24°	=	108°
carpets	2.5	x	24°	=	60°
other things	1	x	24°	=	24°

32 We played 10 hockey matches
(a)   We won 5 and lost 3. How many did we draw?
(b)   How many degrees are there in a revolution?
(c)   How many degrees are needed for each hockey match?
(d)   Work out the size of the angle for each sector. Then draw a pie chart to show matches won, lost and drawn.

33 There were 24 passengers on a bus.
       11 were English
        6 were Scottish
        4 were Welsh
       and the others were Irish.
(a)   How many degrees are there in revolution?
(b)   What angle is needed for each passenger?
(c)   Work out each sector and draw a pie chart.

34 During a certain week a car salesman sold 3 Mercedes-Benz, 6 Volvos, 5 Peugeots and 1 Lada.
(a)   How many cars did he sell altogether? 15
(b)   What angle is needed for each car? $360/15 = 24°$
(c)   Work out the correct angles for each make of car, and draw a pie chart. $24 \times 3 = 72°$ M

35 Of a group of 18 tourists staying at the Beach Plaza Hotel
       7 were American 140°
       5 were German $20 \times 5 = 100°$
       3 were British 60°
       2 were Italian 40°
       1 was French 20°
Work out the angles and draw a pie chart. American = $20° \times 7 = 140°$

Total = 18
$\frac{360}{18} = 20°$ per tourist.

36 Thirty children were given the choice between three sporting activities. Seven chose athletics, fourteen chose swimming, and the others chose tennis. Draw a pie chart to show this information.

37 On a normal weekday, Simon spends 9 hours working, 2 hours eating, 5 hours relaxing and 8 hours sleeping.
(a)   Draw a column graph or bar chart to show this information.
(b)   Draw a pie chart to show this information.
(c)   How would your own day be divided up? Draw a pie chart to show the number of hours spent doing your own activities.

38 Thirty-six customers spent money at Sally Curren's store. Seventeen paid with cash (notes and coins), eight paid by cheque and the others paid by credit card. Draw a pie chart to show how the money was paid.

39 A market gardener sold 250 crates of cabbages, 150 crates of cauliflowers and 200 crates of lettuces. Work out pie chart angles and draw a pie chart to show this information.
(Clue. What angle is needed for 100 crates? What angle is needed for 50 crates?)

40 Last Tuesday, Granny Growl's shop sold the following numbers of pies

10 chicken and mushroom	16 steak and kidney
8 apple	9 gooseberry
5 plum	

(a) How many pies did the shop sell?

(b) What angle would be needed for each pie in a pie chart?

(c) Draw a pie chart to show the number of pies Granny Growl's shop sold.

41 The areas of the four parts of the United Kingdom (to the nearest thousand square miles) are

England	50000	Scotland	30000
Wales	8000	Northern Ireland	5000

(a) How many thousand square miles is the total area?

(b) Divide 360 by the number of thousand square miles to give the pie chart angle for ONE THOUSAND square miles (to 3 significant figures).

(c) Work out the angles (to the nearest degree) for England, Scotland, Wales and Northern Ireland.

(d) Draw a pie chart to show the information.

42 At the Red Lion Hotel last Wednesday, 120 customers ordered meals.

35 ordered roast pork	29 ordered fried haddock
21 ordered beef curry	19 ordered chicken risotto
16 ordered egg salad	

Draw a pie chart to show this information.

43 Five people had collections of conkers (horse chestnuts). Julie had twice as many as George; Kirk had a third of the number that Julie had; Harriet had as many as George's and Kirk's put together; Imran had four times as many as Kirk. George had 60 conkers.

Construct a pie chart to show how many conkers each person had.

44 Shanta used (on average) $\frac{1}{5}$ of her spending money on clothes, $\frac{1}{8}$ on music tapes, $\frac{9}{40}$ on outings, $\frac{1}{15}$ on magazines, and $\frac{11}{60}$ on food.

She put the rest of her money into National Savings.
Draw a pie chart to illustrate how Shanta used her spending money. Label each sector carefully.
Try these questions

(a) What fraction of her money did she put into National Savings?

(b) If she had a total of £30 spending money, how much did she use for outings?

45 Human blood can be classified into four different blood groups (AB, A, B, O). Each person has blood of a certain group. In the U.K.,

about 2% of the population have blood of group AB,

about 46% have blood of group A,

about 8% have blood of group B,

about 44% have blood of group O.

Using a calculator to work out the correct angles (to the nearest degree), draw a pie chart to illustrate this information.

How to find information from a pie chart

Example (1) Twenty-four people were asked which season of the year they liked the most. A pie chart was made from their replies. It looked like this:-

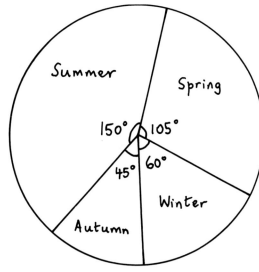

Pie chart to show which season people like most.

What was the total number of people?   24
What angle was needed for this number of people? 360°

What angle was needed for ONE PERSON? $\frac{360}{24} = 15°$

The number of people who liked SUMMER most was $\frac{150}{15} = 10$

Try to work out, in the same way, the numbers who most like spring, autumn and winter.

Example (2) This pie chart shows how members of a class travelled home from school. Some walked, some went by bicycle, some by bus, some by train and some by car. Four members of the class went home by bus.

To find the total number of people in the class
How many travelled by bus?   4
What angle is needed for bus travellers?
   $360 - 108 - 90 - 54 - 36 = 72°$

Each member of the class needs $\frac{72}{4} = 18°$

The total number of people in the class is

   $\frac{360}{18} = 20$

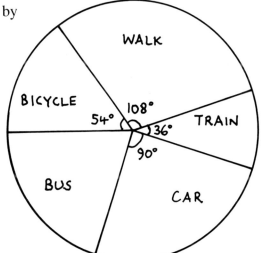

Pie chart to show how members of a class travelled home from school.

To find how many people walked
How many travelled by bus?   4
What angle is needed for bus travellers?
   $360 - 108 - 90 - 54 - 36 = 72°$

Each member of the class needs $\frac{72}{4} = 18°$

Number of people walking is $\frac{108}{18} = 6$ (Quicker way $\frac{108}{72} \times 4 = 6$)

How many people went by bicycle?
How many people went by car?
How many people went by train?

46 Tim delivered 40 evening newspapers to houses in Longton Avenue.

There were four different newspapers and the numbers of papers he delivered are shown in the pie chart.

Make a list of the different newspapers and write against each how many Tim delivered.

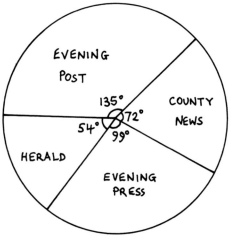

Pie chart showing numbers of newspapers delivered by Tim.

47

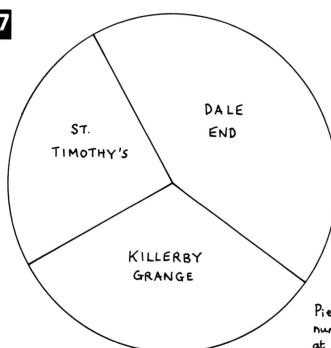

Three schools sent their choirs to sing at a festival.

Altogether there were 72 singers.

Measure the angles in the pie chart and work out how many singers came from each school.

(Clue. What size of angle would ONE singer need?)

Pie chart to show numbers of singers at a festival.

48 Form 3B at Willowbank School made a list of all their pets and then drew a pie chart to show the numbers.

There was only <u>one</u> snake in the list.

Write down the names of the different pets and work out how many there were of each.

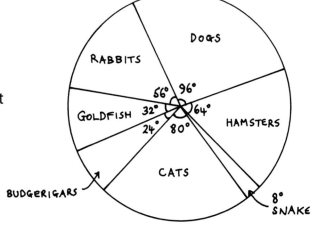

Pie chart to show numbers of pets owned by Form 3B.

49 This pie chart shows how an alloy (called 'nichrome') is made up of three different metals.

Find what percentage of the alloy is
- (a) chromium
- (b) iron
- (c) nickel

(Clue. Percent means out of 100)

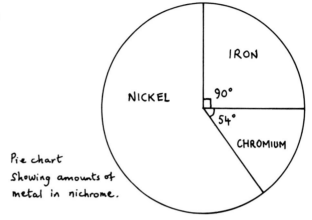

Pie chart showing amounts of metal in nichrome.

50

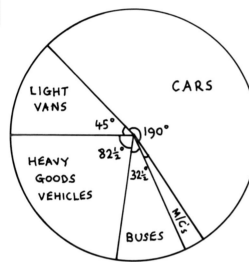

Pie chart showing numbers of vehicles passing the house.

Pete, Derek and Sam did a survey of vehicles passing along the road outside their house. They watched for 10 minutes and recorded 144 vehicles, noting which sorts they were. Then they made a pie chart to illustrate their survey.

Copy this list and write down how many of each sort of vehicle they recorded.
- Number of buses
- Number of cars
- Number of heavy goods vehicles
- Number of light vans
- Number of motorcycles (M/C's)

51 Eighteen people were served drinks at a bonfire party.

Measure the angles, and, from your results, find out how many people had each kind of drink.

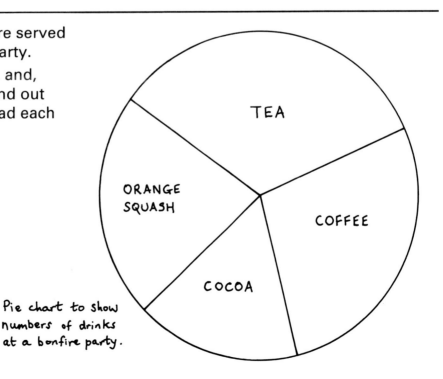

Pie chart to show numbers of drinks at a bonfire party.

LINE GRAPHS

(Use 2mm graph paper for questions in this section)

AXES AND COORDINATES

A graph normally has two AXES (pronounced ax-eez) which are straight lines from which everything else can be measured.

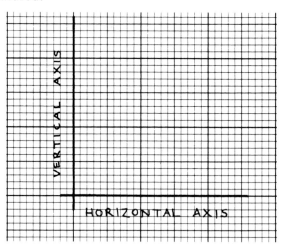

The axis going along the bottom is the **HORIZONTAL AXIS** (also called the x axis).

The axis going up the left-hand side is the **VERTICAL AXIS** (also called the y axis).

Each axis is numbered in a special way. Different graphs have different kinds of numbering.

Most graph paper is ruled with thick and thin lines. Axes should always be drawn along the thickest lines, if possible.

This is a very simple pair of axes

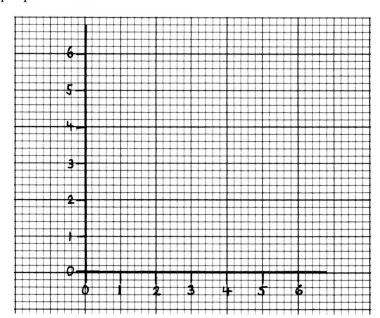

A line graph is usually made up of points (dots) called **COORDINATES.** The coordinates are joined up with lines.

The position of a point on a graph is found by counting along the horizontal axis and then up the vertical axis. A point should be a small, accurate dot, but a ring can be placed round it to show where it is.

Drawing a point on a graph is called **PLOTTING** the point.

The coordinates of the point in the next picture are (4,3). The point has been plotted by counting 4 along the horizontal axis and 3 up the vertical axis

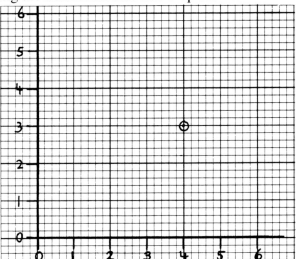

The SCALE of each axis in this example is:-
1 cm to represent 1 unit.
Each axis in each graph has its own scale.

52 Write down the coordinates of each of these points, e.g. A (1,2)

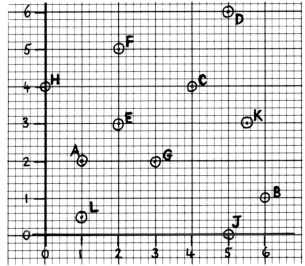

53 Draw axes like the ones in question 52.

Plot points (0,5), (1,4), (2,3), (3,2), (4,1), (5,0).

Join these points with a straight line to make a graph.

54 (a) Copy these axes.
(b) Plot the points
(0.5, 10)
(1, 15)
(1.5, 20)
(2, 25)
(2.5, 30)
(3, 35)
(3.5, 40)

(c) Join the points together with a straight line to make a graph.

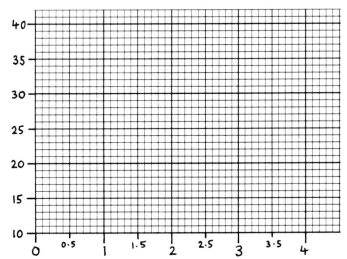

MAKING SENSE OF THE SQUARES

This is an example of an axis used for a graph:-

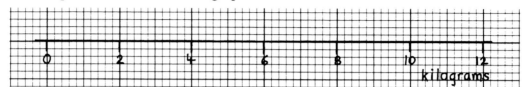

On this axis, 1cm represents 1kg. (Each centimetre along the axis means a mass of 1 kilogram).

Each large (bold) square 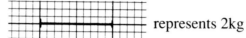 represents 2kg

Each small square ⊢⊢ represents $\frac{2}{10} = 0.2$kg

Before studying a graph, **ALWAYS MAKE SURE WHAT THE LENGTH OF EACH SMALL SQUARE REPRESENTS.**

e.g.(2)

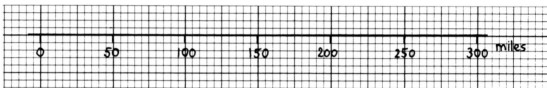

On this axis, 1cm represents 25 miles.
Each large square represents 50 miles.

Each small square represents $\frac{50}{10} = 5$ miles.

---

55 Look at each of these axes and write down
  (i) what each large (2 cm) square represents.
  (ii) what each small square represents.
In part (e), give both your answers in MINUTES.

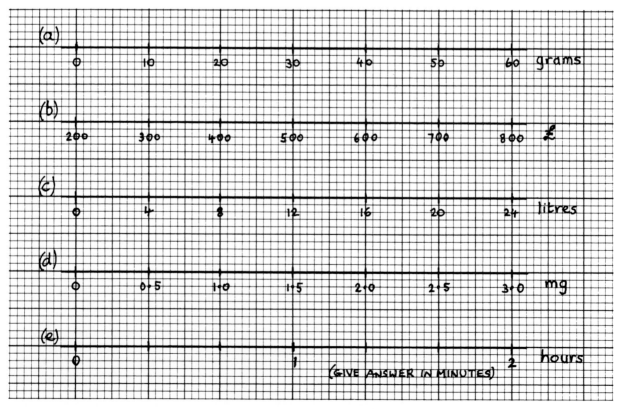

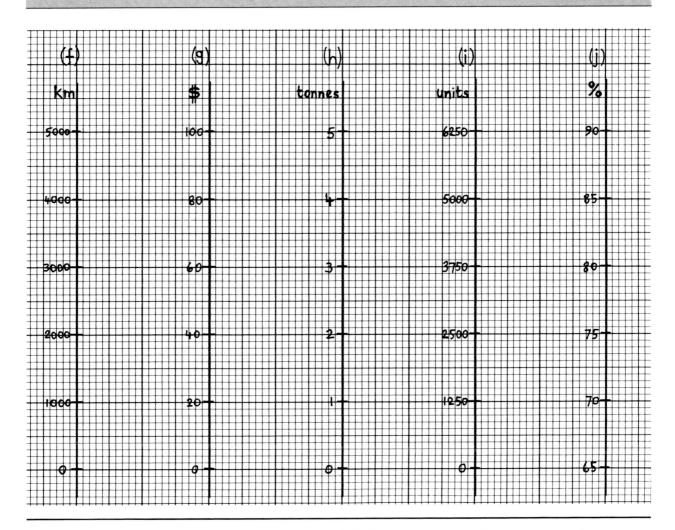

56 (a) Copy each axis and complete it with the correct numbers on each large (2 cm) square.

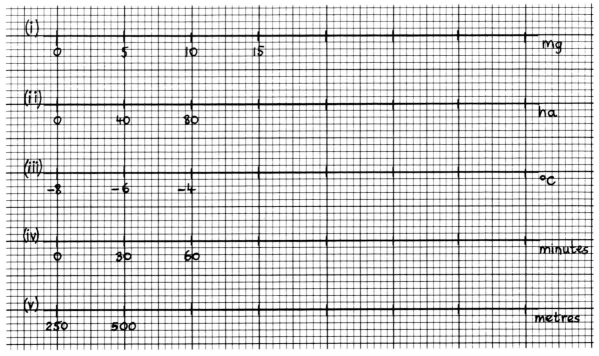

(b) For each of the axes in part (a), write down
(i) what each large square represents.
(ii) what each small square represents.

LINE GRAPHS

This is a graph to show the profits of Pigg & Cowie Ltd.

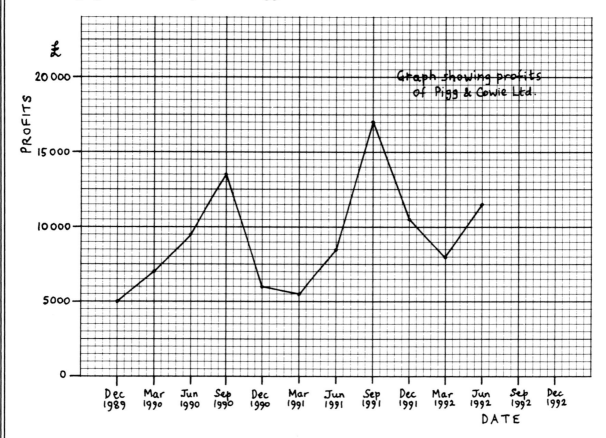

The profits have been noted every three months (every quarter of a year).

The horizontal axis shows DATE with 1 cm to stand for (or represent) each quarter of a year.

The vertical axis shows PROFITS in pounds (£) with 2cm to represent £5000.

In December 1989 the profits were £5000. This gives the point (Dec 1989, 5000).

In March 1990 the profits were £7000. This gives the point (Mar 1990, 7000), etc.

The points are joined with lines to give a line graph.

———————

Some facts and estimates can be noted from the graph, e.g.

(i)   Pigg & Cowie Ltd tend to make more profit in the spring and summer than they do in the autumn and winter.

(ii)   The profits generally increase (get larger) each year.

(iii)   The largest quarterly increase in profit was between June and September 1991.

(iv)   The largest quarterly decrease in profit was between September and December 1990.

(v)   If 1992 followed the usual pattern (or trend) the profits for September 1992 could be estimated at about £20000. What about December 1992?

57

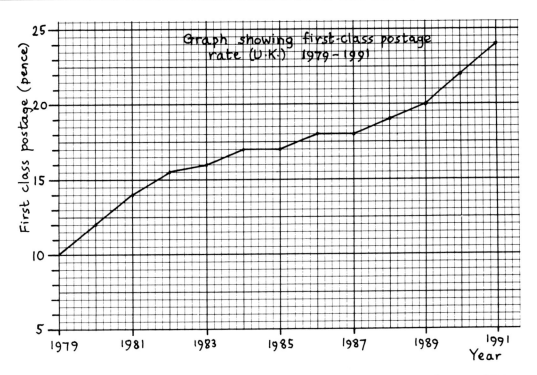

This graph shows the postage rate (U.K.) for a first class letter from 1979 to 1991. Write down
(a) what distance on the horizontal axis represents 1 year.
(b) what amount of money on the vertical axis is represented by 2cm.
(c) the first class postage rate for 1980.
(d) the first class postage rate for 1986.
(e) the year in which the postage rate was 19p.
(f) the year in which the postage rate was 16p.
(g) by which year the postage rate had doubled the 1979 rate.
(h) in which years there was no increase in the rate.

58 When Martin was ill, his temperature was taken every morning (a.m.) and every evening (p.m.). The thermometer readings were

Wednesday a.m.	38.3°C	Friday p.m.	37.9°C
Wednesday p.m.	38.6°C	Saturday a.m.	37.1°C
Thursday a.m.	38.4°C	Saturday p.m.	37.3°C
Thursday p.m.	39.1°C	Sunday a.m.	36.8°C
Friday a.m.	37.5°C	Sunday p.m.	36.9°C

Copy these axes, making sure that each axis is drawn along a thick graph line. Mark the axes with the correct days, temperatures, etc. Plot Martin's temperature for each morning and evening. Then join each point to the next with a dotted straight line to make a temperature graph.

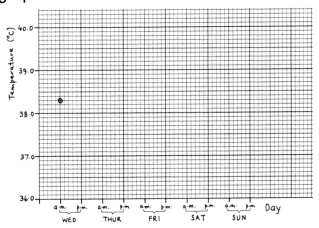

59

(a) Copy the axes shown below. Make sure that each axis is drawn along a thick graph line. Mark the axes with the correct names and numbers.

(b) The air pressure, in millibars, was measured with a barometer every day from 8th to 21st April.
The table on the right shows the dates and pressures.

(c) From the information in the table, plot points.
Start with the point (8,990) to show a pressure of 990mb on the 8th April. Then plot (9,982) and continue until all the points are correctly plotted.

(d) Join each point to the next with a straight line.
Then give your graph a title.

Date	Pressure (mb)
8	990
9	982
10	996
11	1012
12	1018
13	1016
14	1000
15	1000
16	1026
17	1032
18	1028
19	1018
20	1010
21	1014

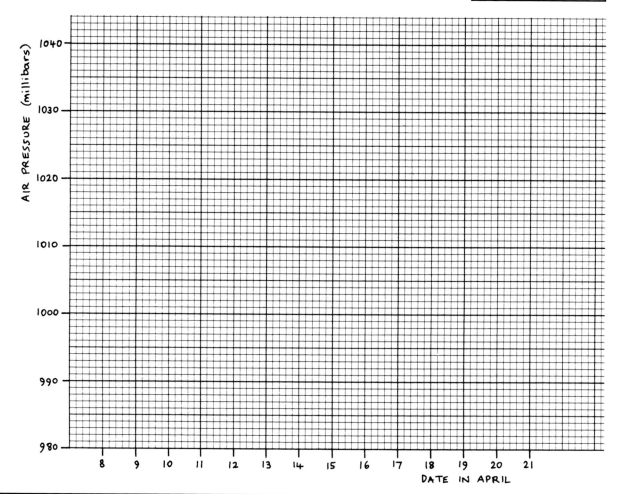

60 A boy's height, in centimetres, at various ages is shown in the table on the right.

(a) On 2mm graph paper, draw axes for a graph.
Horizontal axis: AGE, 0 to 16 years, with 1cm to represent 1 year.
Vertical axis: HEIGHT (cm), 0 to 200cm, with 1cm to represent 20cm.

(b) On the vertical (HEIGHT) axis, what does each small square represent?

(c) Find the coordinates of each point by looking at the table. At age 0, the boy's height was 40cm. This gives the point (0,40). At age 2, his height was 56cm, giving the point (2,56), etc.

Age	Height (cm)
0	40
2	56
4	88
6	112
8	124
10	132
12	136
14	152
16	180

(d)   Plot all the points. Then join each point to the next with a straight line.
(e)   Between which two ages did the boy grow the fastest?
(f)   Between which two ages did the boy grow the most slowly?
(g)   From your graph, estimate the boy's height at
        (i) 3 years of age.
        (ii) 13 years of age.

61 The heights of the tide in the Severn Estuary were calculated for every third day in August, beginning on August 1. The dates and heights were

August 1 ....9.8m   August 19 ....12.0m
August 4 ....10.7m   August 22 ....13.3m
August 7 ....12.2m   August 25 ....12.7m
August 10 .....13.1m   August 28 ....10.3m
August 13 .....11.6m   August 31 ......8.7m
August 16 .....10.0m

Using graph paper with 2mm squares, draw axes for a graph.

Horizontal axis to show DATE (each day from August 1 to August 31, with two small squares for each day).

Vertical axis to show HEIGHT OF TIDE (metres) from 8.0m to 14.0m with 2cm (10 small squares) for 1.0 metre.

Plot points from the list above, starting with (1, 9.8). When all the points are plotted, join each point to the next to make a graph.

From the graph
(a)   estimate the height of the tide on August 9.
(b)   estimate the height of the tide on August 29.
(c)   write down the dates when the height of the tide was approximately 11.0m.

62 The table below shows the total population (to the nearest 0.1 million) of the U.K., recorded at 20 year intervals from 1841.

Date	Population
1841	20.2 million
1861	24.5 million
1881	31.0 million
1901	38.2 million
1921	44.0 million
1941	—
1961	52.7 million
1981	55.8 million

(a)   With horizontal axis for DATE (years) with 2cm to represent 20 years, and vertical axis for POPULATION (millions of people) from 20 million to 60 million with 4cm to represent 10 million people, plot points and join to make a graph.
(b)   In which period of 20 years did the population increase at the greatest rate?
(c)   From the graph, estimate the population of the U.K. in
        (i)   1891
        (ii)   1911
        (iii) 1941
        (iv)   2001
(d)   Why was the population not counted in 1941? (This is a question for history enthusiasts!)

63 Lucy put £100 into a savings account which paid 10% compound interest each year.

Nicola put £100 into a savings account which paid 15% simple interest each year.

The graph shows the amounts that Lucy's and Nicola's £100 would have grown to after 1, 2, 3, 4, etc., years. Lucy's is the broken curved line graph; Nicola's is the straight line graph.

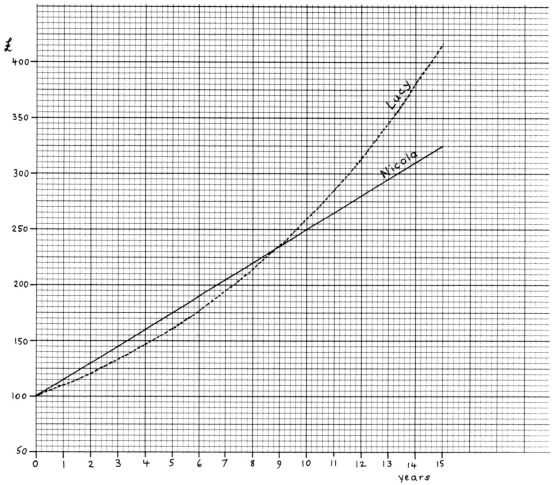

From Lucy's graph, find
(a) the amount of her savings after 4 years.
(b) the amount of her savings after 9 years.
(c) how long she would have to wait before her savings doubled .
(d) how long she would have to wait before her savings trebled (×3).
(e) how much she would have in her account after 5 years if she had saved £250 instead of £100.

From Nicola's graph, find
(f) the amount of her savings after 3 years.
(g) the amount of her savings after 11 years.
(h) how long she would have to wait before her savings doubled.
(i) how long she would have to wait before her savings trebled.

From both graphs, find
(j) who would have the larger amount after 5 years, and how much more she would have.
(k) who would have the larger amount after 12 years, and how much more she would have.

64 A glass of hot water was left to cool and the temperature of the water was measured every 10 minutes. The results are shown in the table.

Draw axes for a graph.
Horizontal: TIME, 0 to 120 minutes with 1cm for 10 min.
Vertical: TEMPERATURE, 20°C to 60°C with 2cm for 5°C.

Plot points and join with a <u>smooth curve</u>.

NOTE. It is usually easier to draw a curve from <u>inside</u> the curve.

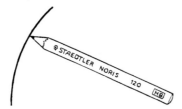

Time (min)	Temperature (°C)
0	59.0
10	52.25
20	47.5
30	43.25
40	39.5
50	37.25
60	35.0
70	33.5
80	32.25
90	30.75
100	29.5
110	28.75
120	28.5

65 An elastic band 8.2cm long was hung from a hook and various masses were hung on the bottom of the band. The masses and lengths of band were noted.

(a) Copy and complete the table.
The stretch is found by subtracting 8.2cm from the length of the band each time, e.g. with 200g mass, the stretch is
9.5 – 8.2 = 1.3cm

Mass (g)	Length (cm)	Stretch (cm)
0	8.2	0
100	8.7	0.5
200	9.5	1.3
300	10.6	
400	11.6	
500	13.2	
600	14.9	
700	16.8	
800	19.0	
900	21.1	

(b) Draw a horizontal axis for MASS with 1cm to represent 100g.
Draw a vertical axis for STRETCH with 1cm to represent 1cm.
(c) Plot the points from the Mass and Stretch columns in the table.
Join the points as nearly as you can with a curved line.
(d) From the graph, estimate the stretch of the elastic band with a mass of
      (i)   440g
      (ii)   760g
      (iii)   1000g

66 A mass was attached to the end of a piece of string to make a simple pendulum. The pendulum was then swung from side to side and the number of swings in ½ minute (30 seconds) was noted. The length of string was changed and the experiment was repeated. The results are shown in the table on the right.

Length of string (cm)	Swings in ½ minute
10	86
20	60
30	49
40	44
50	40
75	34
100	29
150	24
200	21

Draw axes for a graph.
Horizontal axis: LENGTH OF STRING (cm) with 2cm representing 25cm.
Vertical axis: SWINGS IN ½ MINUTE with 1cm representing 5 swings.
Plot the points from the table and join them as accurately as possible with a smooth curved line.

67 A tank was used to store and supply oil. At midnight each night the volume of oil in the tank was checked and recorded.

The graph shows the volumes recorded for the ends of each day from 7th to 20th November.

<u>Example.</u> The volume of oil at the end of the 14th November was 290 litres. At the end of the 15th November it was 240 litres, showing a decrease in volume of 50 litres during the 15th.

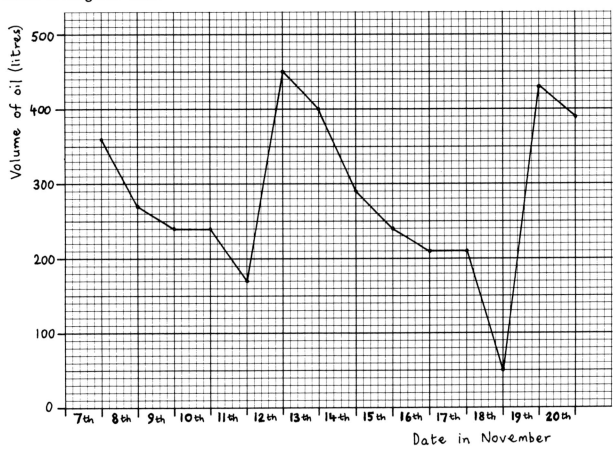

Look at the graph and try these questions:-

(a) What was the volume of oil recorded at the end of each of these days?
  (i) 8th November
  (ii) 13th November
  (iii) 18th November

(b) What was the decrease in volume during each of these days?
  (i) 8th November
  (ii) 14th November
  (iii) 20th November

(c) On which date was the decrease in volume the same as
  (i) 15th November?
  (ii) 16th November?

(d) On which date did the volume decrease the most?

(e) The tank was refilled on the 12th. On which other date do you think it was refilled?

(f) On the 12th, 350 litres of oil were put into the tank. What volume of oil was used (taken out) on that day?

(g) No oil was either put into the tank or taken out of it on a Sunday. Which two dates were Sundays?

(h) On which <u>day</u> (not date) each week was the tank refilled?

68 The graph shows the frequency of vibrations (measured in hertz (Hz) <u>or</u> vibrations per second) of the notes from A at the bottom of the bass clef to E at the top of the treble clef (The higher the note, the greater the frequency; the lowest note is on the far left, the highest on the far right).

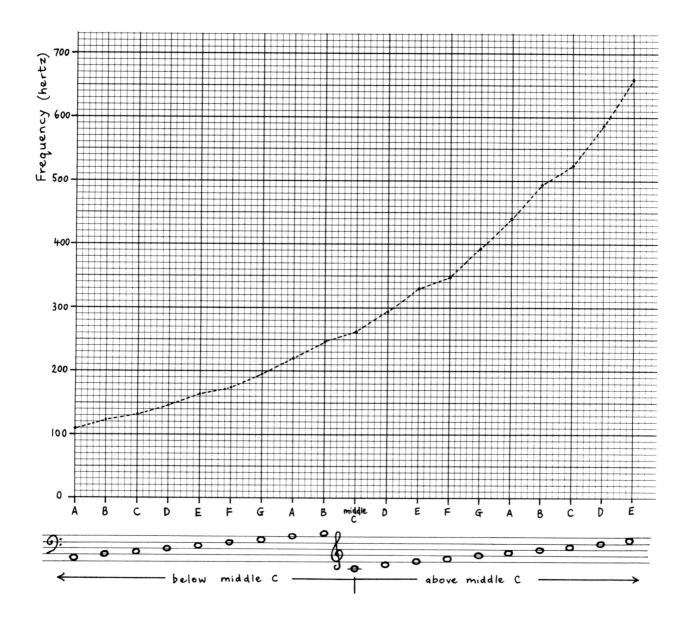

(a) From the graph, find the frequency of
(i) middle C, (ii) F above middle C, (iii) D below middle C,
(iv) E above the C above middle C, (v) G below middle C.

(b) Find which note has an approximate frequency of
(i) 330 Hz, (ii) 130 Hz, (iii) 590 Hz, (iv) 175 Hz, (v) 495 Hz

(c) (i) What are the frequencies of the three different A's? (ii) What do you notice about these frequencies? (iii) What is the frequency of the next A below the ones in the graph? (iv) What is the frequency of the next A above the ones in the graph?

(d) F sharp (F#) has a frequency roughly halfway between the frequencies of F and G. What is the approximate frequency of the F sharp above middle C?

(e) Which note has an approximate frequency of
(i) 625 Hz, (ii) 210 Hz, (iii) 470 Hz ?

Choosing a suitable scale

If you are not given a scale (what represents what on each axis), choose your own.

(a) Look at each axis separately.

(b) Find what the lowest and highest amounts (minimum and maximum) are likely to be. Then look at the number of available squares (or centimetres) and decide what amount each square (or centimetre) should represent.

(c) Choose a <u>simple</u> amount for each square (or centimetre), e.g. 1, 2, 5, 10, 100, etc. It is very difficult to understand a graph if it is made out in complicated units.

(d) You should aim for as large a graph as possible, but not one which is too large for the page.

(e) If your paper is longer than it is wide, see if the graph would fit better the other way on.

---

69 (a) Ten pupils were each given a sample of aluminium metal and were asked to measure (i) the mass, and (ii) the volume of the sample. These were the results:-

Pupil	Mass (g)	Volume (cm³)
A	182	67
B	258	96
C	303	146
D	441	163
E	578	215
F	660	244
G	817	282
H	1000	370
I	1179	437
J	1335	495

(b) Choosing suitable scales for horizontal axis (VOLUME) and vertical axis (MASS), plot these results and join the points with the most likely correct straight line.

(c) From your graph, find
  (i) the volume of a sample of aluminium whose mass is 900g.
  (ii) the mass of a sample of aluminium whose volume is 195cm³.

(d) By finding the gradient of the graph (vertical distance ÷ horizontal distance), or by dividing a mass by its equivalent volume, find the density of aluminium.

(e) Which two pupils made a mistake with their measurements?

---

70 The solubility of a substance is the mass of the substance, in grams, which will dissolve in 100 grams of water.

A certain salt was dissolved in water at six different temperatures. The results were

Temperature (°C)	Solubility g/100g
0	29
20	34
40	41
60	51
80	62
100	77

With temperature on the horizontal axis, plot points and join to form a smooth curve.

From the graph, find the solubility of the salt
  (a) at 50°C
  (b) at 66°C

CONVERSION GRAPHS

A conversion graph is used to convert one kind of unit to another, e.g. 8 kilometres is approximately the same distance as 5 miles. Draw a graph to convert kilometres to miles, marking KILOMETRES from 0 to 50 on the horizontal axis with 1cm representing 5km, and MILES from 0 to 30 on the vertical axis with 1cm representing 5 miles.

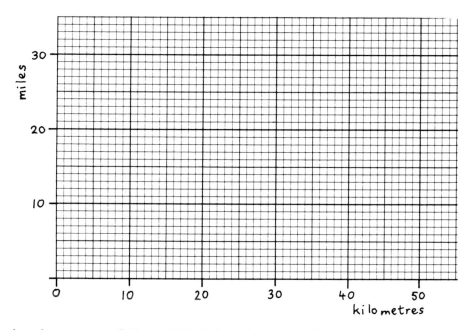

Always number the axes carefully and label them (put what they mean, e.g. kilometres, etc.).

To draw a conversion graph, at least TWO POINTS must be found. First of all, 0 km is the same distance as 0 miles, so the point (0,0) can be marked on the graph.

NOTE (0,0) is often a point on a conversion graph BUT NOT ALWAYS.

From the information given in the question, 8km is the same distance as 5 miles, so the point (8,5) can be marked. If these two points are joined with a straight line, the result is a conversion graph,

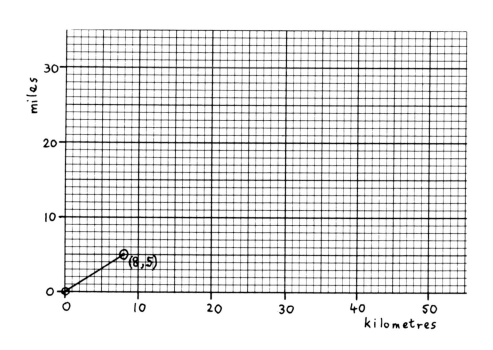

but this graph is very small, so it is better to find some larger values. This can be done by multiplying the kilometres and the miles by the same number, e.g. multiplying by 6 gives 8km x 6 = 48km, and 5 miles x 6 = 30 miles. The point (48,30) can be marked and joined up to give a sensibly-sized graph. Remember to give the graph a title.

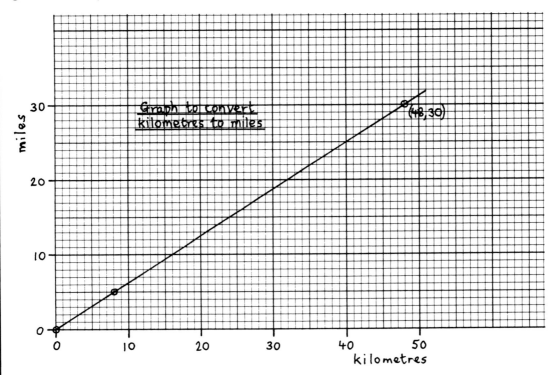

Distances can now be converted by using the graph,

e.g. Express 30km in miles.

To do this, find 30 on the kilometres axis. Draw a vertical line straight up to the graph, then a horizontal line straight across to the miles axis. This gives a reading of about 19 miles.

30km are roughly equivalent to 19 miles.

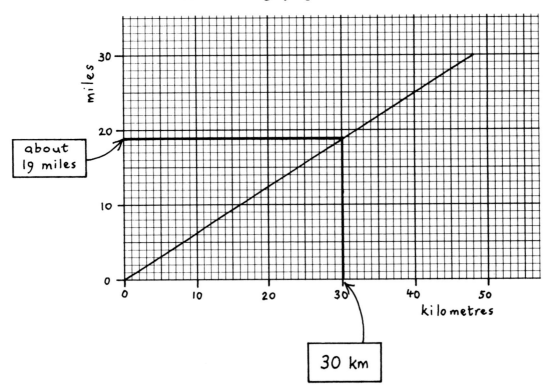

Conversions can be done the other way on

e.g. How many kilometres are roughly equivalent to 9 miles?

How many kilometres are roughly equivalent to 28 miles?

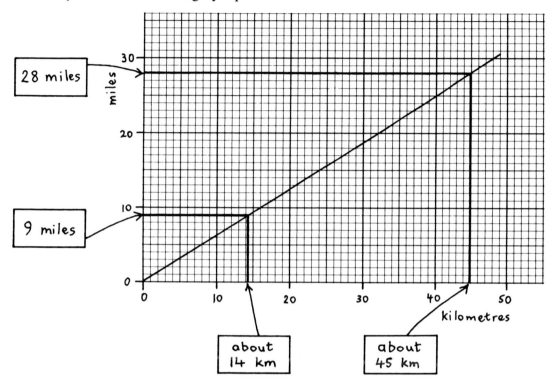

14 kilometres are roughly equivalent to 9 miles.

45 kilometres are roughly equivalent to 28 miles.

---

71 This graph is to convert horse power to watts (and vice versa).

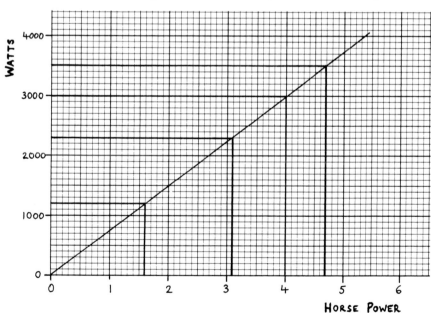

(a) On the horizontal axis, what does each SMALL square represent?

(b) On the vertical axis, what does each SMALL square represent?

(c) From the graph, convert 4 horse power to watts.

(d) Convert 1.6 horse power to watts.

(e) Convert 2300 watts to horse power.

(f) Convert 3500 watts to horse power.

72 This is a graph to convert ounces (oz) into grams (g), or grams into ounces.

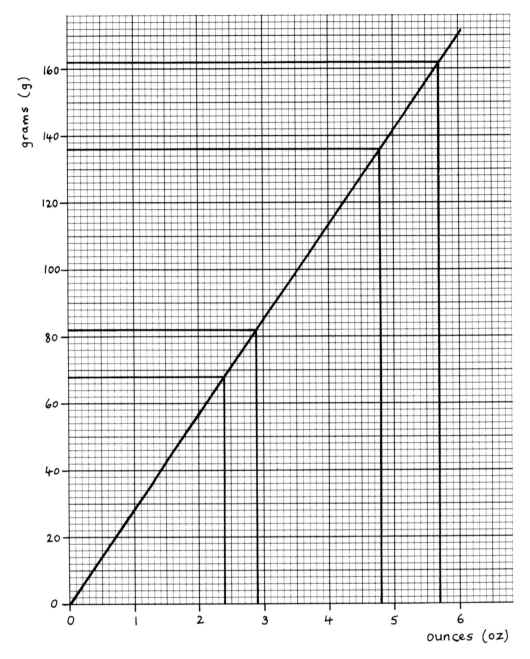

(a) On the horizontal axis, what does each SMALL square represent?

(b) On the vertical axis, what does each SMALL square represent?

(c) How many grams are equivalent to 2.9 ounces?

(d) How many grams are equivalent to 4.8 ounces?

(e) How many ounces are equivalent to 162 grams?

(f) How many ounces are equivalent to 68 grams?

(g) This is a list of ingredients for a chocolate biscuit recipe. Using the graph, write the list again with the amounts in grams.

> 5 oz flour
> 1 oz cocoa
> 2 oz sugar
> 4 oz butter
> Half an egg

73 Draw a graph to convert gallons to litres (and vice versa).
Horizontal axis: 0 to 45 litres, with 2cm to represent 5 litres.
Vertical axis: 0 to 10 gallons, with 2cm to represent 1 gallon.

1 gallon is roughly equivalent to 4.5 litres.
Plot points (0,0) and (45,10). Join these points to form the graph.

From your graph, convert to gallons (a) 30 litres, (b) 17 litres, (c) 41 litres;
convert to litres (d) 7.7 gallons, (e) 2.3 gallons.

---

74 Draw a graph to convert kilograms (kg) into pounds (lb).

Horizontal axis: 0 to 70kg, with 2 cm to represent 10kg.

Vertical axis: 0 to 160 lb, with 1cm to represent 10 lb.

1kg is roughly equivalent to 2.2 lb.

(a) What does each small square on the vertical axis represent?
(b) Convert 16kg to lb.
(c) Convert 66kg to lb.
(d) Convert 114 lb to kg.
(e) Convert 80 lb to kg.
(f) A boy's mass is 100 lb (or 7 stone 2 pounds). What is his mass in kg?
(g) A box of books has a mass of 27kg. What is its mass in lb?
(h) The mass of a certain steam locomotive is 130000 lb.
   (i) What is its mass in kg? (Clue. Look for 130 lb.)
   (ii) What is its mass in tonnes? (Clue. 1 tonne = 1000kg.)

---

75 Draw a graph to convert temperatures Fahrenheit (F) to Celsius (C).
Horizontal axis: –40 to +100 degrees Celsius with 1cm to represent 10 degrees
(–40, –30, –20, –10, 0, +10, etc.).
Vertical axis: –40 to +240 degrees Fahrenheit with 1cm to represent 20 degrees.
–40°C is equivalent to –40°F ⎫ Use this information to draw your graph.
100°C is equivalent to 212°F ⎭
From your graph, convert (a) 0°C to °F, (b) 70°C to °F, (c) 28°C to °F, (d) 180°F to °C,
(e) 108°F to °C.

---

76 This graph converts
hectares (ha) to acres,
and acres to hectares.

From the graph, convert to
acres (a) 6 ha
       (b) 2.6 ha
       (c) 4.7 ha

Convert to hectares
       (d) 8.8 acres
       (e) 19 acres

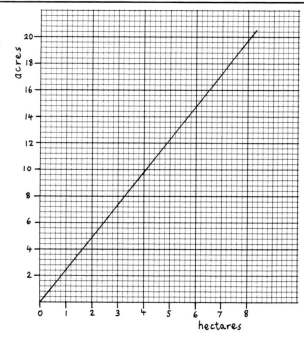

77 For a certain type of ticket, a railway company charges 18p per mile.
Draw axes for a conversion graph for distance (miles) and cost (pence).
Horizontal axis: 0 to 80 miles with 2cm for 10 miles.
Vertical axis: 0 to 1500 pence with 1cm for 100 pence.

(a) By working out the cost for 10 miles and the cost for 80 miles, draw a conversion graph to calculate the rail fare for any distance up to 80 miles.

(b) From your graph, find the approximate rail fare for each of these distances. Give answers in £.
(i)   62 miles
(ii) 37 miles
(iii) 20 miles
(iv) 73 miles

(c) From your graph, find the approximate number of miles that can be travelled for a cost of
(i)   £7.40
(ii) £5.00
(iii) £9.50

---

78 A teacher marks a test out of 80 and wishes to convert his marks into percentages. Draw a conversion graph with marks on the horizontal axis (1cm for 5 marks) and percentages on the vertical axis (1cm for 5%).
0 marks are equivalent to 0%
80 marks are equivalent to 100%

From your graph, find

(a) the percentage scored by a pupil with 45 marks out of 80.
(b) the percentage scored by a pupil with 56 marks out of 80.
(c) the marks out of 80 which will give 78%.

(d) To move into a higher stream, a pupil needs to score 85%. Darren gets 69 marks out of 80. Will he move into a higher stream?
(e) Anyone who scores less than 45% must take the test again. Amanda scores 37 out of 80. Will she have to take the test again?

---

79 One square metre is roughly equivalent to eleven square feet. Using 2cm to represent 1 square metre, and 1cm to represent 5 square feet, draw a graph to convert square feet to square metres, and vice versa.

From your graph,

(a) convert 3.0 square metres into square feet.
(b) convert 5.5 square metres into square feet.
(c) convert 74 square feet into square metres.
(d) convert 47 square feet into square metres.

(e) A rug has an area of 23 square feet. What is its area in square metres?
(f) The length of each side of a square flower bed is 2.5 metres.
(i) Calculate the area of the flower bed in square metres.
(ii) From your graph, find the approximate area of the flower bed in square feet.
(g) An artist takes two paintings to an exhibition. One has an area of 38.5 square feet; the other has an area of 3.6 square metres. Which painting has the larger area?

80 A gas company charges each customer a fixed amount (called a standing charge) of £10, and then charges 50p for each unit of gas the customer uses.

For a customer who uses 0 units, the charge is £10, giving the point (0,10) on the graph.

For a customer who uses 300 units, the total charge is £10.00 + (50p X 300) = £10 + £150 = £160, giving the point (300,160).

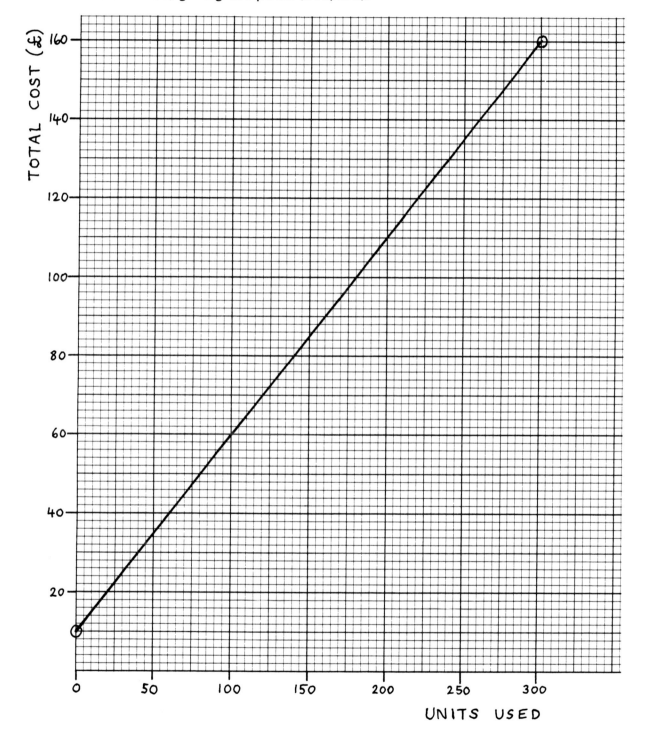

From the graph, find out approximately

(a) the total charge for a customer who uses 70 units.
(b) the total charge for a customer who uses 195 units.
(c) how many units could be used for a total charge of £142.
(d) how many units could be used for a total charge of £78.

81 The quarterly (every 3 months) total charge made by an electricity company is
£15 standing charge (fixed amount),
8p for each unit of electricity used.

Draw a units/total charge graph.

Horizontal axis: Units of electricity, 0 to 4000 units (1cm for 250 units).

Vertical axis: Total charge £0 to £350 (1cm for £25).

(Clue. What is the total charge if 0 units are used? What is the total charge if 4000 units are used?)

From your graph, find
(a)   the total charge if 2500 units are used.
(b)   the total charge if 1200 units are used.
(c)   the total charge if 3650 units are used.
(d)   the number of units which could be used for a total charge of £150.

---

82 A taxi driver charges each customer £1.50 for booking his taxi, and then 50p for each mile the customer travels.
Draw a distance/fare graph for calculating how much the taxi driver charges for different lengths of journey.

On the horizontal axis, mark DISTANCE in miles with 1cm to represent 1 mile.

On the vertical axis, mark FARE in £ with 2cm to represent £1.

Start your graph with the taxi fare for going 0 miles.

From your graph, find
(a)   the fare for a journey of 5 miles.
(b)   the fare for a journey of 14 miles.
(c)   the fare for a journey of 6.6 miles.
(d)   the distance travelled for £6.00.
(e)   the distance travelled for £3.50.

---

83 In the Republic of Slurpia, the unit of currency (money) is the grunt (Gr).
Today's exchange rate is: one U.K. pound sterling (£1) is equivalent to 4.5 grunts (4.5 Gr).

Choosing a suitable scale for each axis (see top of page 36), draw a currency conversion graph (pounds to grunts and vice versa).

From your graph, find
(a)   the equivalent of 58.5 Gr in £ sterling.
(b)   the equivalent of £9 in Gr.
(c)   how much 29 Gr are worth in £.
(d)   how much £114 is worth in Gr (Clue. Divide by 10).
(e)   A U.K. holidaymaker wants to obtain 700 Gr to spend when he is in Slurpia.
       How much, in £, will he have to pay for this amount?
       (Clue. Find 70 Gr on the graph.)
(f)   A certain music cassette costs £4.80, in the U.K. and 23 Gr in Slurpia.
       In which country is it more expensive?

100 pence (100p) = 1 pound (£1)
100 sizzles (100sz) = 1 grunt (1 Gr)
(g)   What is the rough equivalent of 32sz in pence?
(h)   What is the rough equivalent of 11p in sizzles?

84 This graph shows the time of day at different longitudes around the World when it is 12.00 noon (1200 hours) in London (U.K.) which is on longitude 0°.

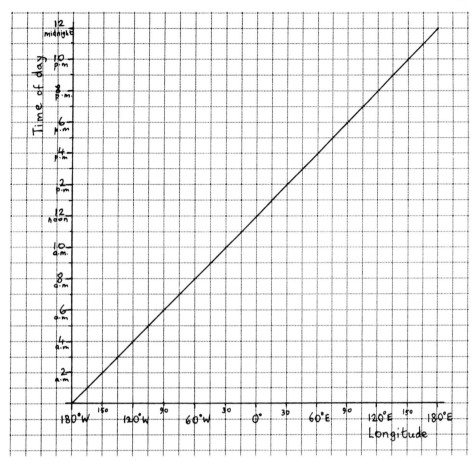

(a) How many degrees of longitude does each square on the horizontal axis represent?

From the graph, find the time (to the nearest hour) in these places when it is 12.00 noon in London:-

(b) Guatemala City (Guatemala), longitude 91°W.

(c) Manila (Phillipines), longitude 121°E.

(d) Kuwait (Kuwait), longitude 47°E.

(e) Port of Spain (Trinidad & Tobago), longitude 62°W.

(f) Brazzaville (Congo), longitude 15°E.

In this list of places, the time is given when it is 12.00 noon in London.
Find the approximate longitude of each place:-

(g) Pago Pago (American Samoa), 1 a.m.

(h) Port Moresby (Papua New Guinea), 10 p.m.

(i) Mexico City (Mexico), 5 a.m.

(j) Islamabad (Pakistan), 5 p.m.

(k) Yangon (Myanmar), 6.30 p.m.

(l) An aircraft sets off from London at 12.00 noon and flies to Rio de Janeiro (Brazil), longitude 43°W. The flight takes 11 hours. When the aircraft arrives in Rio de Janeiro (i) what time is it in London?
(ii) what time is it in Rio de Janeiro?

(m) At 12.00 noon in London, a man wants to telephone a friend in Los Angeles (U.S.A.), longitude 118°W. Why might this not be a good idea?

85 A car started on a journey with a full tank of 57 litres of petrol, and consumed the petrol at a steady rate.

After going 190km it had 42 litres of petrol left.

After going a further 140km it had 31 litres left.

(a) Draw axes for a graph, choosing a suitable scale for each axis (from 0 to 800km on the DISTANCE axis, and from 0 to 60 litres on the PETROL LEFT IN TANK axis).

(b) Plot points for distance and petrol left in tank, and join them to make a straight line graph.

(c) The car continued its journey until it had gone a total of 650km.
At this point its tank was filled up again. Complete the graph to show this information.

(d) From the graph, find
    (i)   the amount of petrol left in the tank when the car had gone 250km.
    (ii) the distance the car had gone when it had 24 litres of petrol left.

(e) If the car's petrol tank had not been refilled, how far would the car have gone altogether before it ran out of petrol? Draw a dotted line on the graph to show this.

---

86 A telephone company charges each customer every quarter of a year
    (a) a fixed rental fee of £23,
    (b) 4.5 pence for each unit of telephone calls made.

Choosing suitable scales, draw axes for a graph (horizontal: UNITS USED, up to 1600 units; vertical: CHARGES (£) up to £100.

Draw a graph to show charges made for number of units used.

From the graph, find
    (i)   the charge to a customer who uses 650 units.
    (ii) the charge to a customer who uses 1200 units.
    (iii) the number of units used by a customer who is charged £59.

---

87 (You will need an electronic calculator).

A medium wave signal from a radio transmitter can be found on a radio dial either by <u>wavelength</u> (in metres) or <u>frequency</u> (in kilohertz).

To convert wavelength to frequency, divide 300000 by the wavelength (in m). This gives the frequency (in kHz).

(a) Draw axes for a frequency/wavelength conversion graph for medium wave transmitters.

Horizontal axis: Wavelength (metres) from 200m to 500m, with 4cm to represent 100m.

Vertical axis: Frequency (kilohertz) from 600kHz to 1500kHz, with 2cm to represent 100kHz.

(b) To plot some points on the graph, start at 200m. Divide 300000 by 200 to give the frequency. Then plot (200,   ). Then try 250m, 300m, etc., up to 500m. Join the points with a smooth curve.

(c) Radio Flab broadcasts on 215m. What is its frequency?

(d) Radio Toddly transmits on a frequency of 950kHz. What is its wavelength?

TRAVEL GRAPHS

A travel graph is a way of recording a journey. It shows the **TIME** and the **DISTANCE FROM A CERTAIN PLACE.** From these, the SPEED of a journey can also be found.

TIME is shown on the horizontal (x) axis.

DISTANCE FROM A CERTAIN PLACE is shown on the vertical (y) axis.

A travel graph goes from LEFT TO RIGHT (and <u>never</u> straight up).

e.g. Draw axes for a travel graph. <u>Time</u> starting at 0900 (9.00 a.m.) with 1cm to represent $\frac{1}{2}$ hour. <u>Distance from Sutcliffe</u> starting at 0 with 2cm to represent 5km. Astbury is 14km from Sutcliffe.

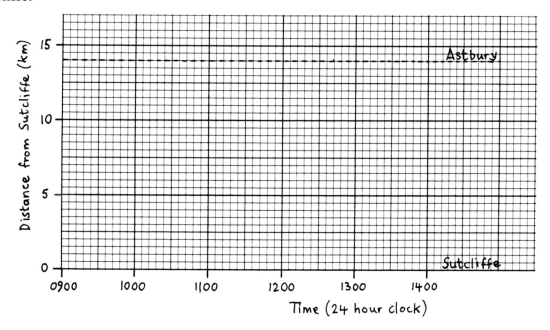

Edward sets off from Sutcliffe at 1000 and walks to Astbury, arriving there at 1330. Draw a travel graph of Edward's journey by marking the points (1000, 0) and (1330, 14) and joining them. This line is Edward's travel graph.

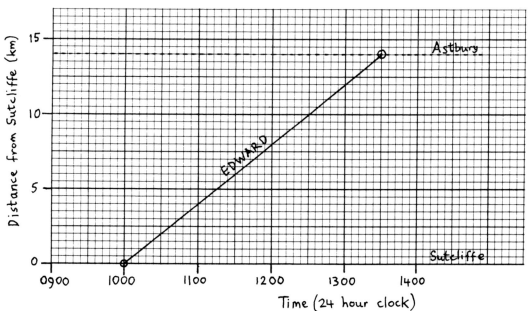

Edward's SPEED can be found by seeing what DISTANCE he goes in a certain TIME. Choose an <u>easy</u> time if possible (e.g. 1 hour, 1 second, etc.).

$$\text{SPEED} = \frac{\text{DISTANCE}}{\text{TIME}}$$

This amount is the **GRADIENT** of the graph.
The steeper the gradient (or slope) of the graph, the greater the speed.

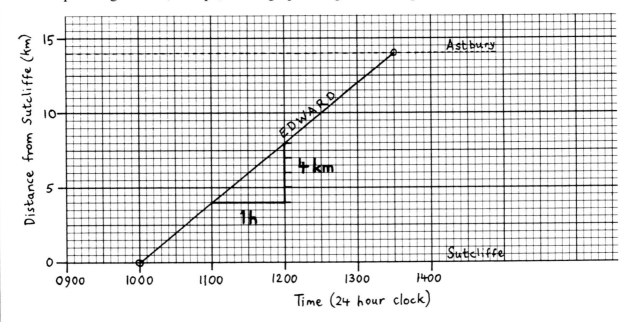

In 1 hour Edward goes 4km, so his

$$\text{SPEED} = \frac{4}{1} = 4\text{km/h}$$

For more work on speed, see page 50.
Emily sets off from Sutcliffe at 0930 to walk to Astbury. She walks for 10km at a speed of 5km/h, then stops for half an hour to eat her sandwiches. Then she finishes her journey at 4km/h.

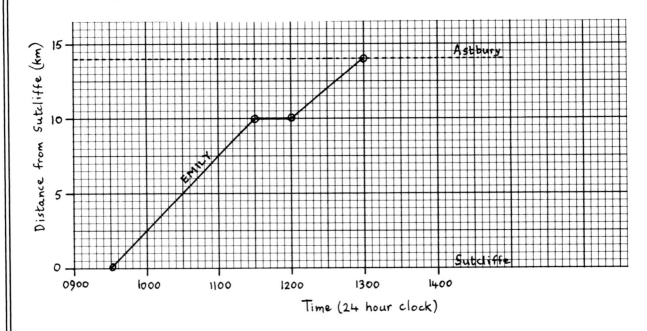

Matthew sets off from Astbury at 1000 and cycles to Sutcliffe at 14km/h.

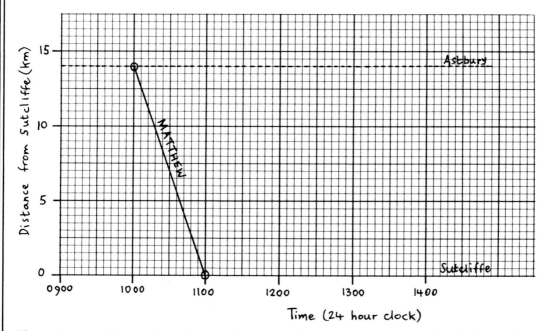

If two (or more) travel graphs are drawn on the same axes, some other information can be found.

e.g. If Emily and Matthew are on the same route, at what time do they meet and how far from Sutcliffe do they meet?

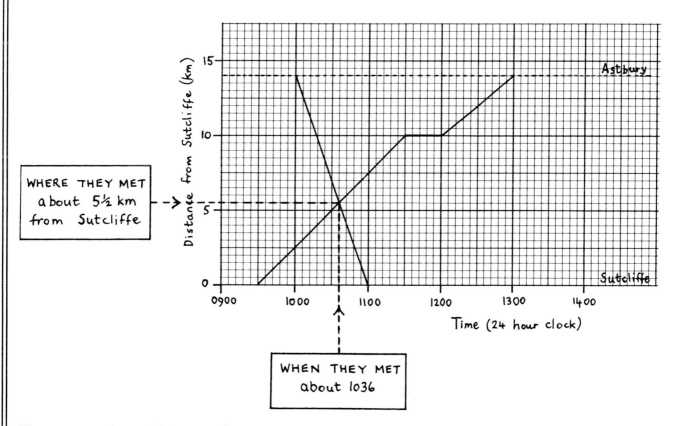

WHERE THEY MET
about 5½ km
from Sutcliffe

WHEN THEY MET
about 1036

They meet at about 1036 about 5¹/₂km from Sutcliffe.

How to find SPEED from a travel graph

e.g. Find the speed of this cyclist.

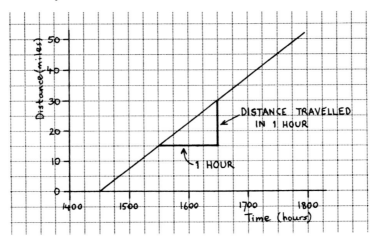

1) Find an easy length of time, if possible 1 second, 1 hour, 10 seconds, etc.
2) From the travel graph, draw a horizontal line to represent your chosen time (1 hour in this example).
3) Complete a right-angled triangle by drawing a vertical line to meet the graph. Measure the distance represented by the vertical line.
4) Divide the distance (vertical) by the time (horizontal).

$$\text{SPEED} = \frac{15}{1} = 15 \text{ miles/hour}$$

<u>BE CAREFUL.</u> If, for example, you want the speed in miles/h but have not a whole hour on your graph, choose an easy time, e.g. Find the speed of this aeroplane.

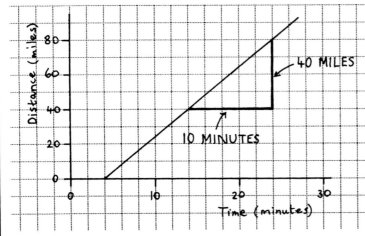

Time chosen: 10 minutes
Distance: 40 miles
In 10 minutes, aeroplane goes
     40 miles.
In 1 hour (or 60 min), aeroplane goes
     40 x 6 = 240 miles.

$$\text{Speed} = \frac{240}{1} = 240 \text{ miles/h.}$$

Note. For measuring speed, it does not matter whether the graph has a
     positive gradient   or a   negative gradient

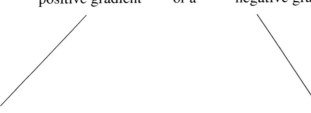

SPEED is always $\dfrac{\text{DISTANCE}}{\text{TIME}}$ (<u>or</u> vertical ÷ horizontal)

88

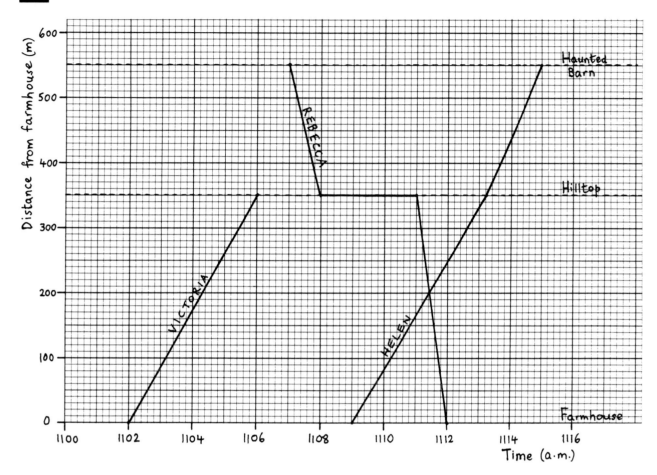

Look at the graph. Then copy and complete these sentences.

(a) Victoria set off from the farmhouse and walked to the..........

(b) She set off at 1102 a.m. and arrived at.........a.m.

(c) Rebecca set off running from the haunted barn at ....a.m. and reached the
hilltop at.........a.m.

(d) She rested on the hilltop for.........minutes.

(e) She reached the.........at 1112 a.m.

(f) Helen set off from the.........at.........a.m. and walked and ran to the haunted
barn, arriving there at.........a.m.

(g) The hilltop is.........m from the farmhouse.

(h) The hilltop is.........m from the haunted barn.

(i) The haunted barn is.........m from the farmhouse.

(j) Helen passed Rebecca.........m from the hilltop.

(k) Rebecca reached the hilltop.........minutes after Victoria.

(l) If Victoria had gone on walking towards the haunted barn at the same speed,
instead of stopping at the hilltop, she would have met Rebecca.........m from the
haunted barn.

89 (a) Draw axes for a travel graph.
Horizontal axis: Time from 1000 to 1500, with 3cm to represent 1 hour.
Vertical axis: Distance from Home: 0 to 10 miles with 1cm to represent 1 mile.

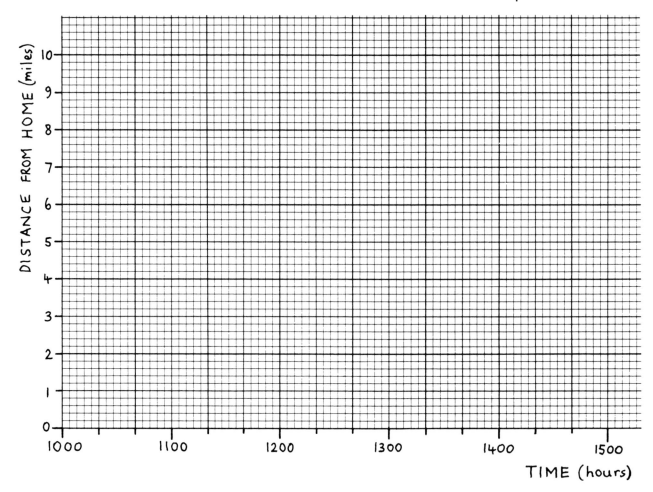

(b) What length of time, in minutes, is represented by 1cm on the horizontal axis?

(c) Uncle John's house is 10 miles from Home. Draw a dotted horizontal line to represent Uncle John's house.

(d) Tim set off from Home at 1100 and walked to Uncle John's house at 3 miles/h. How far from home was he at 1200?

(e) Draw a travel graph of Tim's journey from Home to Uncle John's house. Write TIM on the graph.

(f) Sam set off from Home at 1230 and cycled to Uncle John's house, arriving there at 1320. Draw Sam's travel graph and mark it SAM.

(g) When did Tim arrive at Uncle John's house?

(h) What was Sam's average speed in miles/h? (Clue: How far did he go in ½hour?)

(j) If Sam and Tim took the same route
    (i)   at what time did Sam pass Tim?
    (ii) how far from Home did Sam pass Tim?
    (iii) how far from Uncle John's house did Sam pass Tim?

90 (a) Draw axes exactly like the ones in question 89.
Mark Uncle John's house in the same way.

(b) Emma set off from Home at 1020 and walked towards Uncle John's house at 4 miles/h. At 1120 she stopped and rested for half an hour. Then she set off again and completed her walk, arriving at Uncle John's house at 1350. She stayed there until 1440. Then Uncle John drove her home in his car. She arrived at Home at 1500. Draw a travel graph of Emma's journey.

(c) Mike set off from <u>Uncle John's house</u> at 1050 and walked home at a steady speed of 3 miles/h. Draw Mike's travel graph.

(d) At what speed did Emma walk on the second part of her journey (from when she finished resting until arriving at Uncle John's house)?

(e) How long did Emma stay at Uncle John's house?

(f) What was the average speed of the car?

(g) At what time did Mike arrive home?

(h) If Emma and Mike were on the same route
  (i)   at what time did they meet?
  (ii) how far from Home were they when they met?

91 This graph represents a runner who runs a straight 1500m (A), then rests (B), then runs back again (C).

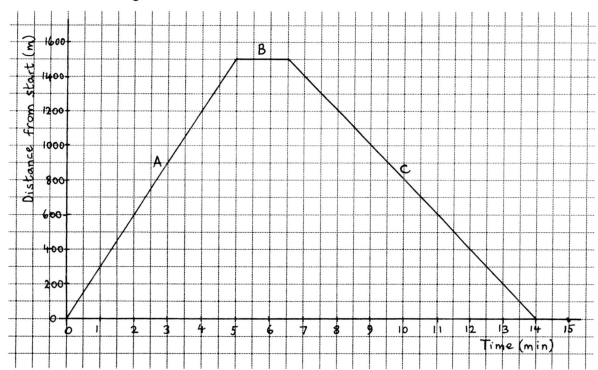

(a) On the time axis, what does one square represent?

(b) On the distance axis, what does one square represent?

(c) How far has the runner gone after 1 minute?

(d) What is his speed for part A in metres/minute?

(e) How long does he rest?

(f) What is the total distance he has run after 10 minutes?

(g) What is his speed for part C in m/min?

(h) At this speed (if he could keep it up!) how many metres would he go in 1 hour?

(i) What is his speed for part C in km/h?

(j) For what total length of time is he running?

92

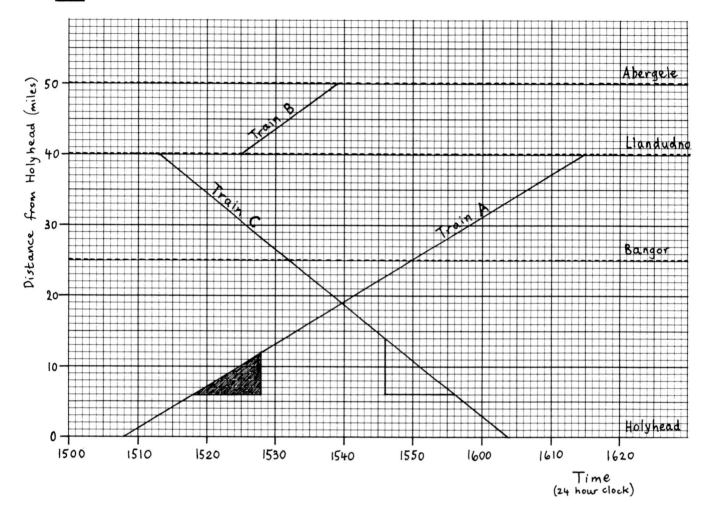

Look at the graph and try the questions.

(a)   At what time does train A leave Holyhead?

(b)   At what time does train B arrive in Abergele?

(c)   At what time does train C leave Bangor?

(d)   At what time does train A arrive in Llandudno?

(e)   Look at the <u>shaded</u> triangle. Then copy and complete these sentences

    (i)   In 10 minutes, train A goes.........miles.

    (ii)   In 1 hour (= 6 X 10 minutes), train A goes.........miles.

    (iii)   Average speed of train A is.........miles/hour.

(f)   Look at the <u>unshaded</u> triangle and find the average speed of train C in miles/h.

(g)   How many minutes are there between the departure of train C from Llandudno and the departure of train B from Llandudno?

(h)   What is the distance from Abergele to Bangor?

(i)   At what time do trains A and C pass one another?

(j)   How far from Holyhead are trains A and C when they pass one another?

<u>Note.</u> Names are pronounced (roughly): <u>Holly</u>-hed, <u>Bang</u>-ger, Klan-<u>did</u>-no, Abber-<u>gelly</u>.

93 (a) Draw axes for a travel graph.
Time: From 1800 to 2200 with 3cm to represent 1 hour.
Distance from York: From 0 to 80 miles with 1cm to represent 10 miles.
Northallerton is 30 miles from York.
Newcastle is 80 miles from York.

(b) Bert sets off from York in his truck at 1820 on a journey to Newcastle. He drives at an average speed of 30 miles/h until he reaches Northallerton where he stops for 40 minutes to eat a pork pie and read his evening paper. Then he continues his journey to Newcastle at 40 miles/h. Draw a travel graph of Bert's journey.

(c) Sally sets off from Newcastle at 1940 and drives to York, arriving there at 2140. Draw a travel graph of Sally's journey, using the same axes which were used for Bert's journey.

(d) At what time does Bert reach Newcastle?

(e) What is Sally's average speed?

(f) If Sally and Bert are both travelling on the same road,
   (i) how far from York does Sally pass Bert?
   (ii) how far from Newcastle does Sally pass Bert?
   (iii) at what time does Sally pass Bert?

---

94 (a) Draw axes for a travel graph.
Time: 0800 to 1200 with 1cm to represent $1/4$ hour.
Distance from Moscow: 0 to 500 miles with 1cm to represent 50 miles.
Kiev is 450 miles from Moscow.

(b) An aircraft leaves Moscow at 0800 and lands at Kiev at 0930. Draw a travel graph to represent this journey.

(c) The aircraft waits for $3/4$ hour at Kiev. Continue the graph to show this.

(d) After its $3/4$ hour wait, the aircraft returns to Moscow. It arrives in Moscow at 1130. Continue the graph to show this.

(e) How far does the aircraft go in the first hour of its outward journey (from Moscow to Kiev)?

(f) What is its speed in miles/h on its outward journey?

(g) How far does it go in the last hour of its homeward journey (from Kiev to Moscow)?

(h) What is its speed in miles/h on its homeward journey?

(i) <u>Calculation for enthusiasts</u>

$$\text{Average speed} = \frac{\text{Total distance}}{\text{Total time}}$$

By finding the total distance the aircraft has flown and the total time (in hours) it has actually been in the air, work out the average speed for the round trip (from Moscow to Kiev and back again). Give answer in miles/h to the nearest whole number.

(a) Anna and Caroline live at a house called Hollycroft.
Draw axes for a travel graph.
Time: 1400 to 2000 with 1cm representing $\frac{1}{2}$ hour.
Distance from Hollycroft: 0 to 90km with 1cm representing 5km.

(b) Jenny's house is 80km from Hollycroft. The hypermarket is 30km from Hollycroft. Draw dotted horizontal lines to show Jenny's house and the hypermarket.

(c) Anna and Caroline left Hollycroft together at 1430 and travelled towards Jenny's house. For the first 40km of their journey they went in a car at a speed of 80km/h. Then they walked at 6km/h for 1h 30 min. By this time it was raining so they stopped and sheltered. Draw a travel graph for Anna and Caroline.

(d) Jenny left her house at 1700 and travelled in her van towards Hollycroft at 50km/h. She picked up Anna and Caroline and all three went on together (at 50km/h) to the hypermarket where they did half an hour's shopping. Then they all set off and drove to Hollycroft, arriving there at 1900. Draw a travel graph for the journey of Jenny's van, using the same axes as before.

(e) Look at your graphs and try to answer these questions:-
  (i) How far were Anna and Caroline from Hollycroft when they were sheltering?
  (ii) At what time did Jenny pick up Anna and Caroline?
  (iii) At what speed did the van do the last part of the journey, from the hypermarket to Hollycroft?

 (a) Draw axes for a travel graph.
Horizontal axis: TIME from 1100 to 1340 with 1cm to represent 10 minutes.
Vertical axis: DISTANCE FROM LUGANO with 1cm to represent 5km.

(b) On the horizontal axis, what length of time does one small square represent?

(c) Write LUGANO on the right-hand end of the horizontal axis.
Como is 25km from Lugano. Mark Como as a dotted horizontal line and write COMO on the right-hand end of the line.
Bergamo is 72km from Lugano. Mark Bergamo in the same way.

(d) Mario takes off from Lugano in his helicopter at 1100 and flies to Como, arriving there at 1112. He stays in Como for 12 minutes and then flies on to Bergamo. He arrives in Bergamo at 1144.

He takes off again from Bergamo at 1220 and lands at Como 20 minutes later. After waiting there for 32 minutes he takes off again and flies back to Lugano where he arrives at 1324. Draw a travel graph of Mario's journey.

(e) Mario's house is in the village of Merone which is between Como and Bergamo and is 13km from Como. His children like to wave to him as he flies over the house. At what times should they wave to make sure he sees them?
(Clue. Draw a dotted line to represent Merone.)

97

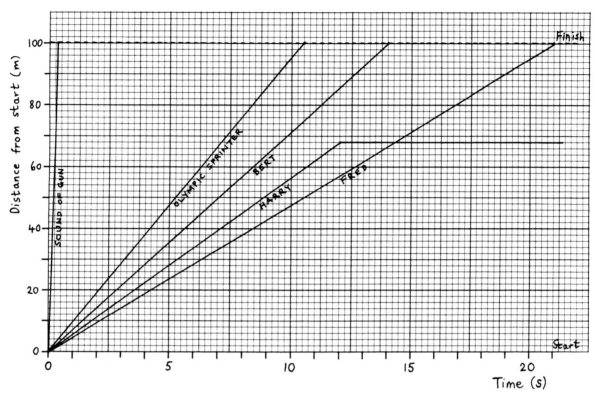

The travel graph shows a race over a distance of 100 metres. A gun is fired to start the race, and the competitors run as fast as they can.

(a) On the time axis, how many small squares represent 1 second?

(b) On the distance axis, how many metres does each small square represent?

(c) How long does the Olympic sprinter take?

(d) How long does Bert take?

(e) How far has Bert gone after 10 seconds?

(f) From your answer to (e), work out Bert's approximate speed in metres/ second (m/s).

(g) After 10 seconds, how far behind Bert is Fred?

(h) How long after Bert does Fred finish?

(i) Suggest what happens to Harry after 12 seconds.

(j) A person with a stopwatch at the finish line times the race from when he sees the puff of smoke from the starting gun. Suggest why he does not time the race from when he hears the sound of the gun.

98 (a) Martin set off from Kelgrave at 1400 to cycle to Lampston which was 30 miles away.

Draw axes for a travel graph.
Time: 1400 to 1730 with 1cm to represent ¼ hour.
Distance from Kelgrave: 0 to 30 miles with 2cm to represent 5 miles.

At 1515, Martin's bicycle had a puncture which he could not mend. He was exactly half-way to Lampston. He then walked at 4 miles/h to a telephone which was 2 miles further along the road. He telephoned his friend Alan who set off from Kelgrave in his van at 1600 to pick up Martin and his bicycle.

Martin waited at the telephone until Alan arrived in his van at 1630. It took fifteen minutes to load the bicycle on to the van. Then they both set off for Lampston in the van, arriving there at 1715.

(b) Draw a travel graph for each of the people (both on the same axes).

Their graphs will both be the same after they have met at 1630.

(c) What was Martin's speed during the first part of his journey?

(d) When did Martin reach the telephone?

(e) After reaching the telephone, how long did Martin wait for Alan?

(f) At what speed did Alan travel before he reached Martin?

(g) How far was the telephone from Lampston?

(h) At what speed did the van travel on the last stage of the journey?

---

99 Vikkie travelled by train from Reading to Worcester, collected some secret documents from her friend Jessica, then returned to Reading. On her way from Reading, she changed trains at Oxford.

This was her timetable:-

Outward Journey	**Homeward journey**
Reading .... depart 1406	Worcester .... depart 1642
Oxford .... arrive 1436	Reading .... arrive 1824
Oxford .... depart 1448	
Worcester .... arrive 1600	

Draw a travel graph of Vikkie's journeys.
Horizontal axis: Time from 1400 to 1830 with 1cm representing 15 minutes.
Vertical axis: Distance from Reading, with 1cm representing 10 miles.

Oxford is 28 miles from Reading.
Worcester is 84 miles from Reading.

(a) Find the average speed of the train (to the nearest 1 mile/h)
   (i) from Reading to Oxford.
   (ii) from Oxford to Worcester.
   (iii) from Worcester to Reading.

(b) How long did Vikkie's complete mission take from leaving Reading to arriving back in Reading?

(Worcester is pronounced WOOSTER; Reading is pronounced REDDING.)

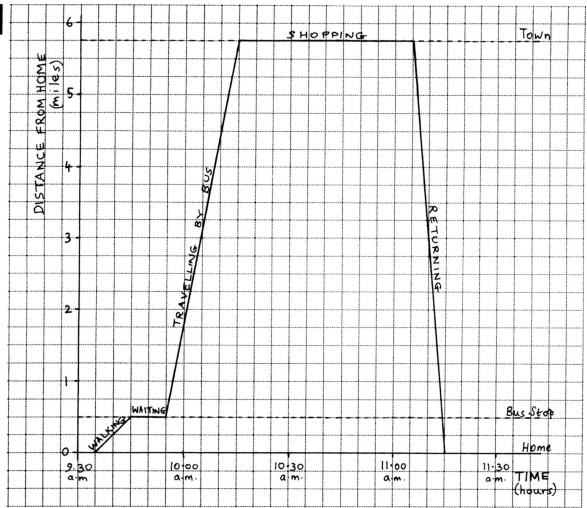

This is a graph to show the journey of Tammie and Sharron who walk from their home to the bus stop, travel by bus to the town, do their shopping and return home by car.

Try these questions.

(a) At what time do they set off from home?

(b) How far is it from home to the bus stop?

(c) How long do they wait for the bus?

(d) How far do they travel by bus?

(e) How long do they spend shopping?

(f) At what time do they set off on their journey home?

(g) What is the distance from the town to home?

(h) How long does the car journey take?

(i) What is the speed of the bus in miles/hour? (Clue. The bus takes 20 minutes, so how far would it go in 60 minutes at the same speed?)

(j) What is the speed of the car in miles/hour?

101 (a) From Auckland, the distances of Wellington, Christchurch and Dunedin are 320 miles, 510 miles and 700 miles respectively. Draw axes for a travel graph with 2cm to represent 1 hour, and 2cm to represent 100 miles. Mark the time axis TIME (h) and the distance axis DISTANCE FROM AUCKLAND (miles). Start the time axis at 0700 (seven o'clock a.m.) and start the distance axis at 0.

(b) Aircraft A leaves Auckland at 0700 and flies to Wellington at a speed of 150 miles/h. It stops at Wellington for 30 minutes, then resumes its flight to Christchurch at the same speed. It stays in Christchurch for 1 hour before returning to Auckland non-stop, arriving there at 1530. Draw the travel graph of Aircraft A.

(c) Aircraft B leaves Dunedin at 0830 and flies to Wellington at 200 miles/h. After waiting at Wellington for $1\frac{1}{2}$ hours it flies on to Auckland at 200 miles/h. Using the same axes, draw the travel graph of aircraft B.

(d) From your graphs, write down the approximate answers to these questions:-
    (i)   At what time does aircraft A arrive in Christchurch?
    (ii)   At what time does aircraft B set off from Wellington?
    (iii) At what time does aircraft A pass over Wellington on its return journey?
    (iv) What is the speed of aircraft A on its return journey to Auckland?
    (v)   How far is it from Wellington to Dunedin?
    (vi) At what time does aircraft B arrive in Auckland?
    (vii) Assuming the aircrafts' flight paths to be approximately the same (but not exactly the same!), at what time does aircraft A pass aircraft B?
    (viii) When aircraft A passes aircraft B, how far from Wellington are the two aircraft?

---

102 Theo and Yugo start off from home at 0930 for a long-distance walk. They walk at 3 miles/h for $2\frac{1}{2}$ miles. Then they stop and rest for 10 minutes. After that, they continue walking at $2\frac{1}{2}$ miles/h.

(a) Draw a horizontal time axis from 0930 to 1130 with 1cm to represent 10 minutes.

(b) Draw a vertical axis for distance from home, marked from 0 miles to 6 miles, with 2cm to represent 1 mile.

(c) Draw the travel graph of Theo and Yugo.

Back at home, their brother Jamie discovers that the walkers have forgotten to take their orange squash. Jamie loads the orange squash on to his bike and sets off at 1024 to catch up with them. He cycles at 7 miles/h. After he has reached them he cycles home and arrives back at 1115.

(d) Using the same axes, draw Jamie's travel graph.

(e) From your graph, find
    (i)   at what time Theo and Yugo stop for a rest.
    (ii) at what time Jamie catches them up.
    (iii) how far from home Jamie catches them up.
    (iv) at what speed Jamie returns home (Clue. What fraction of an hour does he take to do the journey back home?).

103 In each of these travel graphs, find the SPEED. Remember to write down the units (e.g. miles/h, m/s, etc.).

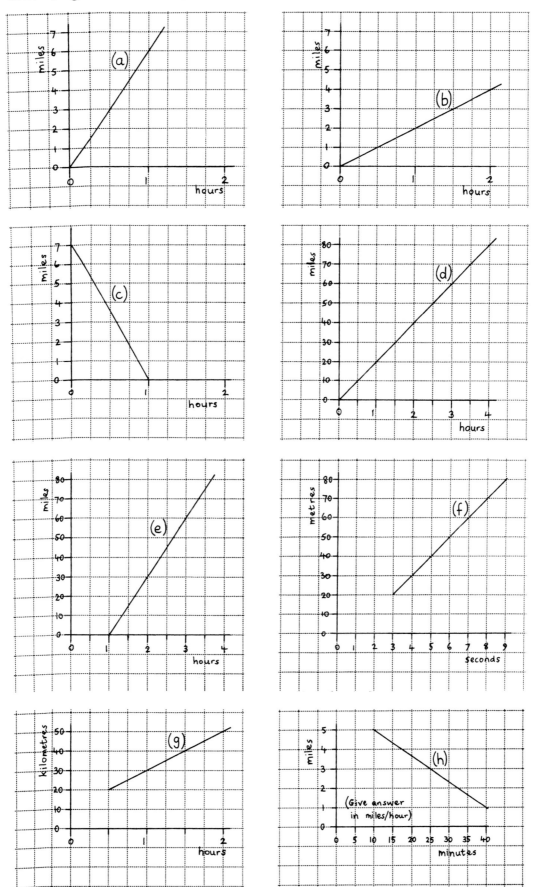

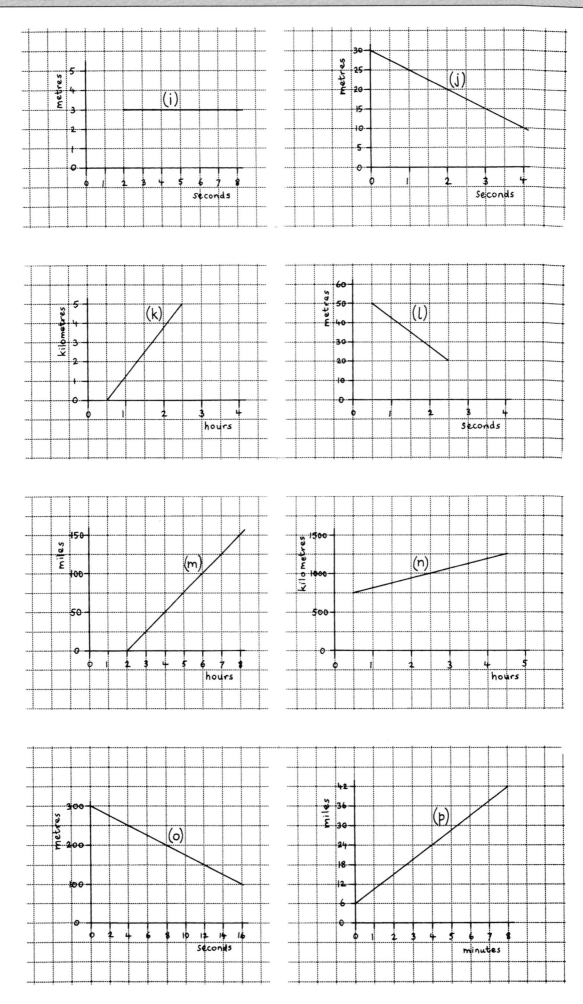

104

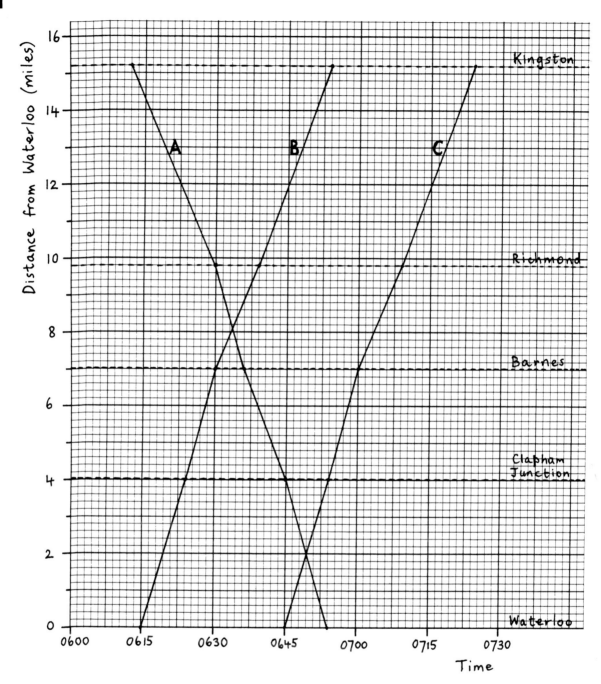

This is a travel graph showing the journeys of three trains between Waterloo and Kingston on Thames.

(a)   On the time axis, what does one small square represent?

(b)   On the distance axis, what does one small square represent?

(c)   Copy and complete these timetables by filling in the dotted lines with the correct times (d means departs, or leaves; a means arrives).

Train A			**Train B**			**Train C**		
Kingston	d	0612	Waterloo	d	0615	Waterloo	d	......
Richmond	d	0630	Clapham Jnc	d	......	Clapham Jnc	d	......
Barnes	d	......	Barnes	d	......	Barnes	d	......
Clapham Jnc	d	......	Richmond	d	......	Richmond	d	......
Waterloo	a	......	Kingston	a	0654	Kingston	a	......

(d) What is the distance from Waterloo to Richmond?

(e) What is the distance from Kingston to Clapham Junction?

(f) When train A passes train B
   (i) roughly what time is it?
   (ii) about how far are they from Barnes?

(g) When train A passes train C
   (i) roughly what time is it?
   (ii) about how far are they from Waterloo?

(h) A man gets off train B at Richmond and waits for train C. How long does he wait?

(i) How much time elapses between the departures of trains A and C from Clapham Junction?

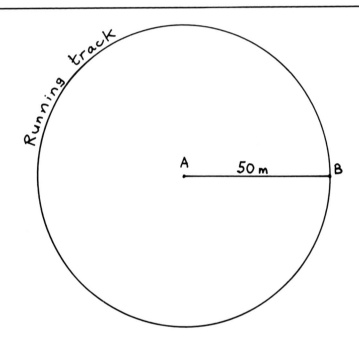

A silly travel graph

A is the centre of a circular running track.

Daniel started at A and walked to B, 50m away, in 30 seconds. Then he ran three times round the running track, taking 4 min 30 sec. After that, he walked back from B to A in 30 sec.

Draw Daniel's travel graph with horizontal axis showing time in seconds (1cm to represent 20s) and vertical axis showing distance from A (1cm to represent 5m).

Try these questions:-

(a) At what speed did Daniel walk from A to B?

(b) Luke walked with Daniel from A to B, then waited at B until Daniel had completed his three circuits, then walked back to A with him.
   What would Luke's travel graph look like?

(c) (A question for people who know how to use π).
   (i) How long is the running track (to the nearest metre)? [$\pi = 3.14$]
   (ii) At what speed did Daniel run? Give your answer to 2 significant figures.